# The Ballad of Sleeping Beauty

Written by Gabriel Benson

Art by Mike Hawthorne

Colors by Michael Atiyeh

Letters by Omar Mediano

Covers by Jeff Amano

But they went anyway.

Every drop of sweat and blood purchased another shot at paradise.

And then ...

A glistening valley.

The perfect place to build their new lives.

The perfect place to raise their children and put the past behind them.

Every storm has its silver lining, but every calm has its storm.

The first winter was especially hard on the town. They had seen many winters before, but none like this. None so hard.

WELCOME TO BRIAR ROSE

None so bitter.

None so utterly alone.

An old Indian came looking for help.

They gave her nothing.

To be fair, they had fought her "kind" before on the way to paradise. Of course, this frail, old woman was hardly a threat to anyone.

I guess they did what they thought they had to do to survive.

And survive they did, though they never spoke of what they had done until it was long forgotten.

Then when the first child of the town was born...

The cutest little girl...

A grand feast was held.

Everyone was invited ...

And then an old memory returned.

Their guilt overwhelmed them.

She never said a word.

And as the day grew long...

... they almost forgot she was even there.

Everyone lavished the child with gifts.

But when the old woman rose to give a gift, they were overcome with shame until they realized ...

... that her gift wasn't a gift after all.

It was a curse.

She promised that the child would fall into a deep slumber on her 18th birthday.

And the town would sleep along with her as punishment for what they had done.

They tried to make her take it back.

The girl grew up to be easy on the eyes and the soul.

A real Beauty.

But sure enough, on her 18th birthday, she fell asleep just as the old woman said she would.

The town soon followed.

From that day forward, no one has seen the town. Like it just disappeared.

Like I said Kid. It's a good story.

Really?

But there's one thing don't fit. . . .

How do you know all this? You told me about that family who tried to escape and turned into dust.

It's a legend.

Drake.

Funny, I thought we was huntin' him.

We are. Go see if the kid is still alive. And let's get out a' here.

Sorry about that kid.

Is he gonna bring my picture back?

Honestly, kid. I'm not even sure he is coming back.

What happened to him? To make him So hard.

That man loved his wife more than I think any man has ever loved any woman.

And when she died . . .

Something in him just broke. And he did what anyone would do...

He went and killed everyone he saw.

See, I don't think Cole would mind dying if it meant he could see her again.

But before he goes, he is gonna hafta kill the man responsible. And that has proved more difficult than you might think.

See. There are many things chasing him.

And sooner or later. Whatever is after him. Just might find him.

If that happens. . .
I have no idea what he might do.

You heard me.

I also told 'em I'd kill him the moment he crossed me. Skin 'em alive I said.

Generous of ya.

I don't have to be generous.

I don't even have to trust him.

Then why we goin'?

You comin' or not? I figured you were itchin' to go.

'Course I'm comin. Just would have been nice if we had talked about it is all.

Guys...

Cole.

Good to see you again. Though I am sorry about the circumstances.

Where's my wife?

Why you hunt us?

Because my wife never hurt anybody.

But we...

And that didn't stop you from hurting her.

He did that?

Lives with it everyday.

Interesting.

So the "boy" convinced Cole to join his silly journey. I didn't think Cole had it in 'im to try and be a hero anymore.

Almost makes me sad that they won't make it there alive.

Haven't you patched somebody up before? Hold him still now.

What kinda trouble you boys get into out there?

Trouble. This is nothin'. We was jus' playin' with the birds.

You got a name pretty lady?

Blue. You are lucky. Those birds out there don't usually leave you alive.

When you see 'em, best to run, for if you follow 'em...

They usually are leading you to hell.

That was funny son. You gotta learn to laugh. What little life you have is meant to be enjoyed.

'Sides you got nothin' to worry about with the law here.

Is the kid gonna die?

Red? Die? You don't know this boy at all do ya?

He's on a mission. He been dyin' since it started. But he ain't gonna finish dyin' 'til it's done. Just like you.

Hard place to find - this town of his. You gotta want to find it. I know men walked right by it without seeing it.

But you...

...I think you need to find it.

You don't know anything about me.

'Course I do. Something bad happened to you once, and you have spent every day since not getting' over it. It don't take no barkeep to see that.

And I am one of the best.

And besides, what other kind of man-

besides a wildly desperate man-

would join Red on his fool's journey?

So you don't believe his story?

Oh, I never said that. You should go see the kid.

So there I was. Coming over this hill. And damn it was hot. Sun so hot, you could fry an egg on my scalp.

And then I hear someone screaming - cursing.

So I pull up my horse. Looking around. Cause I don't see nothin'.

Then I look down, and at my feet is Cole - buried up to his neck in the sand.

Cursin' like a gal with skinny hips givin' birth to a giant.

Now you think he would have asked nicely for me to lend him a hand.

But no, he called me every curse I had ever heard, and a few others that I still don't quite know what he meant.

His way of askin' me to pull him out of there.

Got you to do it? Didn't I?

How you doin' kid?

I think I'll make it.

Good. As soon as you ready to move, we are going to have to get goin'.

Not safe for us to stay here for long.

You always did hate waiting.

Hahaha Served them right treating her like a prized calf like that.

They didn' know what to do. The whole town was either afraid of her, or tryin' to protect her.

So she made 'em pay for it.

She was always fakin' passin out, or playin' dead.

Sounds like she was a great girl.

She was.

The people had kinda givin' up on hopin' that they were gonna be saved.

So they went out and tried to have a good time. But it just never felt right.

And she always knew it.

Then you get chased by some damn "dead Indian".

Get off me, kid.

Sorry.

We almost get ate by devil-spawned birds.

And now Drake is back on our tail.

All I can say is that life has been a tad more interestin' with that kid around.

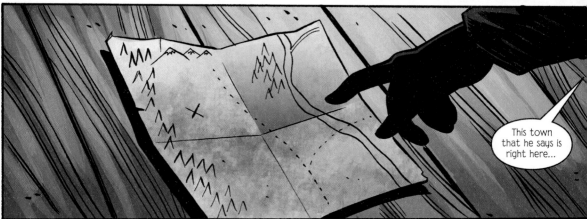

*Her only sin was being born into a town that had made a mistake.*

*Sometimes people are given a choice, and they make it wrong.*

*Sound familiar?*

Where are my friends?

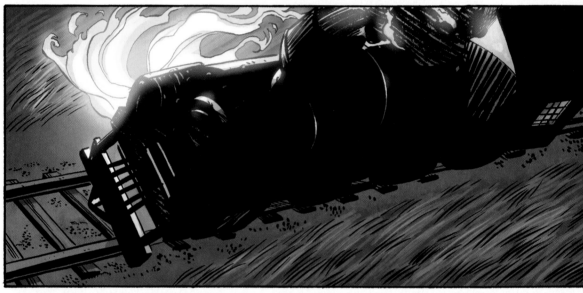

You did it.

It's over.

⟨kof!⟩
⟨kof!⟩

I gotta know ...

Anything pardner. Whatever you want only ...

Just what was that other plan of yours?

⟨kof!⟩
⟨kof!⟩

Heh, heh ...

Kid - look after Cole. He's not as tough as he likes to make out.

Don't let me die like this.

Not far now.

I was afraid you were goin' to give up after...

Like I said. He would have wanted me to.

Cole? Can I ask you somethin'?

Knowin' you - don't see how I have much choice.

Why did you take my picture of Beauty? You been holdin' it tight.

Does she remind you of your wife?

Kid. I'm gonna get you to this town. Walk you to the door where this girl is sleepin', and then you can walk up to her, kiss her on the lips or whatever it is that you be hopin' for.

Then when it's done, I'm gonna leave you.

Just because I am gonna do all that for you, it don't make you Will.

And sure as spit don't make you man enough to talk to me like he would.

Yah!!!!

Kid, get away from me.

No. I believed in you up on those gallows. Thought you were man enough to help me. Thought you were willing to put aside your ghosts. But I see you just want to let them eat you alive.

Kid, I'm warnin' you.

What you gonna do? Kill me too? You killed Drake, but that hasn't eased your pain any. You're still mean and nasty as a rattlesnake.

You got a lot of courage. Knowin' what I am capable of.

I don't think gunnin' me down is gonna kill what's eatin' you inside. And I think you know that.

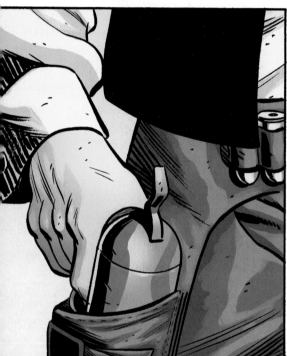

God, I miss him already.

I thought killin' Drake would make the world better. Bring Laura back to me. But she is really gone. Don't think I ever really knew that til right now. You know, your friend Blue told me that I needed to find this town to save my soul. And I think Will thought the same thing.

So I'm gonna do it. I'm gonna get you there.

But you know what still hurts? Not knowin' why. Drake said that to me once. He told me that he had a reason why he killed Laura. But I never found out why.

Cole...

No. Not yet. You wanna know why I'm still mean as a snake? Well, it's because at this point my life has been worth nothin'.

My wife was murdered. I went out to avenge her death, but was huntin' the wrong prey. That just about made me the worst man in the world. See, killin' folks has gotten easy for me. But it still cuts each time. Then I find out a man who I thought was my friend actually killed her. And now, because he's dead, I ain't never gonna know why. Why he killed her. And why he used that act to turn me into a killer.

I don't know what I did to deserve to walk down this path to hell. But I am on it.

So why am I holding that picture? Maybe I did think that savin' her would allow me the chance I missed when I didn't save my wife.

But I know now...

That was only a dream.

You can keep it.

No, kid. I don't want to hold onto that dream anymore.

It's already cost me more than I was willin' to give.

You think I don' regret what I became.

Jus' get it over with.

I'm comin' to you, Laura.

CAWWWW

Drake!

CAWWW
CAWWW
CAWWW

Get out of here, Red.

Everyone, get out of here.

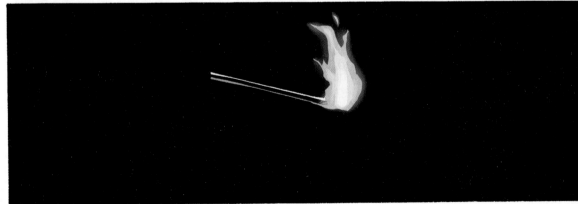

You know
why I hate you...

'Cause no
matter what I did
to you...

You insist
on playing hero.

We have to get these boards off.

Cole, I need your help.

But those people...

You think they're fightin' just for you?

They fight for her. They fight so we can finish this.

There's nothin' you can do that'll chill these old bones.

Open the door, Cole. He's just afraid of what's behind those doors.

Do it. Save her.

I don't know how you keep gettin' up from the grave, but you been tryin' awful hard to keep me from going through these doors.

This is your one chance, Cole. Walk away now and you'll never see my face again.

I walk away now and your stench will haunt me all the days of my life.

No!!!

Stop your whining. You knew it had to end here.

And you... My old friend. You have no idea what I'm afraid of...

# The Ballad Of Sleeping Beauty
## Cover Gallery

Jeff Amano

# The Ballad Of
# Sleeping Beauty

# The Ballad Of Sleeping Beauty

# The Ballad Of Sleeping Beauty

# The Ballad Of Sleeping Beauty

# Afterword

If I had gotten my way, Cole would have been a young prince named Paul, who's destiny it was to rescue the sleeping girl, and save his besieged homeland from the tyranny of the evil that had enslaved the young princess in the most amazing fantasy adventure ever produced!

Sometimes it is good to not get your way. Years later, and too numerous to count attempts at trying to find the right genre to tell my tale, I stumbled onto setting it as a western. (Thanks Jeff!)

But the truth is that while the setting was perfect for the story, the setting was never the reason why my old tale didn't work. It wasn't the genre. It was the story. I wasn't getting to the heart of what those whacky Brothers Grimm were up to.

So I reread it, and reread it, and reread it. (Not hard to do, it 's only three pages!) Finally, I started to get it. They were telling a story about mistakes, what happens when you make one, and how to own up to them. Sure there's other stuff in there, it's three theme-packed pages, but for me it all came down to the mistakes we make in life.

Rather conveniently, my new genre is perfect for tales of redemption. So Paul became Cole, the grizzled gunfighter who must fight his way to save the girl as his final act of redemption. Red would be the one to guide him there, and Drake would be the grim reaper tempting Cole away from the right path.

All seems so simple really. Just took me six years to figure it all out.

The rest was almost too easy as the team around me made everything I wanted to do better than I could have hoped. From Mike Hawthorne's amazing interior work, especially those amazing cliffhanger pages for each book, to Michael Atiyeh's handling of the complicated transitions and flashbacks that I insisted on putting into every issue. And to wrap up each issue in the perfect package were Jeff Amano's striking covers. Each one was better than the next and somehow managed to find the iconic moment for each issue.

In addition to those three amazing guys, this book wouldn't have been possible without the help of everyone else at Beckett for their amazing support and dedication to this book. And while I hate to single out people, as I know I will be forgetting someone I shouldn't, I want to thank Omar Mediano, Jamie Webb, Jenifer Grellhesl and Claire Amano for their belief, support and guidance during this long process.

Finally, I would to thank my family and Courtney Selby for their constant support, and Mike Wood who without his patience I probably would have quit on this project long ago.

Thanks for reading.

Gabriel Benson

# Child and Family Welfare

# Child and Family Welfare

A CASEBOOK

Cognella Casebook Series for the Human Services

Jerry L. Johnson and George Grant, Jr.

*Grand Valley State University*

cognella®

SAN DIEGO

Bassim Hamadeh, CEO and Publisher
Amy Smith, Senior Project Editor
Alia Bales, Production Editor
Jess Estrella, Senior Graphic Designer
Alexa Lucido, Licensing Manager
Natalie Piccotti, Director of Marketing
Kassie Graves, Vice President of Editorial
Jamie Giganti, Director of Academic Publishing

Cover image copyright © 2017 Depositphotos/IgorTishenko.

Printed in the United States of America.

cognella® ACADEMIC PUBLISHING

3970 Sorrento Valley Blvd., Ste. 500, San Diego, CA 92121

*To my wonderful parents, Lee and Joanne Johnson, who continue to encourage and support me in my endeavors. You are the best parents a man could have.*

Jerry L. Johnson

*To my wife, Beverly, who inspires and supports me in all my endeavors. In loving memory of my father and mother, George and Dorothy Grant.*

George Grant, Jr.

# BRIEF CONTENTS

*Preface   xiii*

**1**   A Multiple Systems Approach to Practice in Child Welfare   1

**2**   Child Protective Services   33

**3**   The Adoption of Curtis and William   57

**4**   Inside My Head   75

**5**   A College Experience   91

**6**   Best Practices   107

About the Editors   121

About the Authors   123

# CONTENTS

*Preface xiii*

**1** A Multiple Systems Approach to Practice in Child Welfare 1
Jerry L. Johnson & George Grant, Jr.
Advanced Multiple Systems (AMS) Practice 2
*Sociological Roots 2*
AMS Overview 4
*Multiple Systems Perspective 4*
Dimensions of AMS Assessment 7
*A. Dimension 1: Client Description, Presenting Problem, and*
*Referral 7*
*B. Dimension 2: Treatment/Therapy History 7*
*C. Dimension 3: Substance Use History 8*
*D. Dimension 4: Mental Health History 8*
*E. Dimension 5: Family History 8*
*F. Dimension 6: Social Support and Engagement 9*
*G. Dimension 7: Culture 9*
*H. Dimension 8: Biopsychosocial Connection 9*
Guiding Practice Principles 10
Guiding Practice Principles Explained 11
*First Principle (Umbrella Principle): Healthy Outcomes (and Lives)*
*are Directly Related to People's Connections to Helpful, Supportive*
*Systems, Across a Lifetime 11*
*Client Engagement 14*
*Fostering, Building, or Rediscovering Hopes and Dreams 16*
*Principle A: Clients Are People, Too 18*
*Principle B: Check Your Practice/Professional Privilege at the*
*Door 20*
*Structural and Historical Systems of Privilege and Oppression: Who*
*Holds the Power? 20*
*Principle C: Culturally Respectful and Responsive Client*
*Engagement 22*

*Principle D: Motivation Matters    25*

*1. Precontemplation    26*

*2. Contemplation Stage    28*

*3. Preparation Stage    28*

*4. Action Stage    29*

*5. Maintenance Stage    29*

*6. Relapse Stage    29*

*Last Principle: When All Else Fails, Never Do Anything That*
*Violates the First Principle!    30*

Summary    30

Core Beliefs    30

References    31


**2    Child Protective Services    33**

George Grant, Jr.

Introduction    33

The Intake    33

Mother's Mental Health Needs: The Tate Family    35

*Mother's Mental Health    35*

*Regina Copeland    36*

*The Grandparents    40*

*The Court    41*

*Closing the Case    41*

Infant in Distress: Ryan Wheeler Jr.    42

*A Case Assignment    42*

*Ryan and Deborah    44*

*The Family Across the Street    47*

A Call from School: Curtis and William Hall    49

*A Call from School    49*

*The Hall Home    51*

References    53


**3    The Adoption of Curtis and William    57**

George Grant, Jr.

Introduction    57

What Is Adoption?    58

Adoption Recruiting    59

The Cannon Assessment    60

Social History    61

Child Adoption Assessment    63

*Child Assessment    63*

*Curtis and William Meet the Adoption Worker* 64
Adoption Preparation 66
The Visits 67
The Cannons' Home 68
   *The Adjustment of Curtis and William* 68
   *School* 71
References 73

**4**   Inside My Head: First 24 Hours, A Residential
Placement 75
George Grant, Jr.
Introduction 75
Child Welfare 75
Cori Woodall 77
Raymond 79
Now the Therapy Starts 81
Waiting for Dinner 82
That Evening 85
References 88

**5**   A College Experience 91
Jessica Campbell
Introduction 91
Barriers to Foster Children Attending College 91
What Is Fostering Laker Success? 93
Meet the Life Coach 93
Meeting Kara 94
Next Meeting 97
Basic Needs 98
Home Life 99
Kara in Foster Care 100
Her Final Placement 102
Kara's Second Year of College 103
Kara's Third Year of College with Fostering Laker Success 104
References 105

**6**   Best Practices 107
George Grant, Jr.
Introduction 107
Self-Care 109
   *Robert's First Job* 109
   *Self-Care Continued* 111

*The Stress*   112
Power   112
  *Mary Has Power*   112
William Admitting Mistakes   114
Code of Ethics   116
Janet and The Two Models   117
Conclusion   119
References   119

About the Authors   121

About the Authors   123

# PREFACE

WELCOME TO OUR new Casebook Series for the Human Services. This series of books is designed to improve professional clinical practice education across the human services. As the editors, we are thrilled by our partnership with Cognella to make these books available to educators and students across the human services spectrum.

This text, *Child and Family Welfare: A Casebook*, will enhance the clinical preparation of students and practitioners across the helping professions, who are either presently working with this population or interested in doing so in the future.

As graduate and undergraduate social work educators, we (Johnson and Grant) understand the struggle to find quality clinical practice materials that translate well into a classroom setting. In the past, we used case materials from our practice careers. Then, in the early 2000s we edited and published the Allyn & Bacon Casebook Series between 2005 and 2007. The original Casebook Series covered eight different practice areas (substance abuse, mental health, domestic violence, sexual abuse, adoption, foster care, community practice, and medical social work).

While we were happy with the first series, we wanted to improve its quality and usefulness in the classroom while updating the topics to more closely match current trends. Over the years, we sought and received extensive feedback from readers and faculty adopters about the strengths and weaknesses of the previous series. Most importantly, we asked specific questions about each case's ease of use in the classroom.

In preparing the new series, we relied heavily on this feedback, resulting in the book you are reading and forthcoming Casebooks in the series. We believe the new Casebook Series for the Human Services, as evidenced by this text, published by our friends at Cognella, achieved our goal of enhanced learning opportunities and ease of classroom use.

Our goal is always to give student readers the chance to study, assess, and analyze how experienced practitioners think about practice, struggle to resolve practice dilemmas, and make clinical decisions to meet the needs of their clients. We believe the structure of our cases, written in narrative voice and story format, allows readers access to the minds of experienced practitioners in a way that will improve engagement, assessment, diagnostic, and treatment planning skills, but more importantly enhance the way students think about their clients and practice.

Overall, we intend for the Casebook Series for the Human Services to provide a learning experience that:

1. Provides readers an overview of our previously published Advanced Multiple Systems (AMS) approach to practice (Johnson & Grant, 2005). This practice perspective describes an approach to practice as either a simple guide to working the cases in the Casebooks and/or later in their practice careers.

   More importantly, we define AMS through a series of Guiding Practice Principles, developed by the editors over the course of long careers, study, and experience. Our Guiding Practice Principles offer a way for practitioners to think about and act in practice settings to help guide successful engagement, leading to a positive helping experience for clients and professionals.

2. Offers personal and intimate glimpses into the thinking and actions of experienced practitioners as they work with diverse clients across different practice settings. In working through each case, students have the chance to demonstrate their understanding of the clinical and social issues presented while learning to use high-level "assessment thinking" through the various questions and exercises included to help make sense of each case.

3. Provides multiple opportunities to develop a comprehensive clinical assessment, diagnoses, treatment plans, and emergency plans for a variety of presenting problems from a diverse client group. These exercises also provide excellent opportunities for large and small group discussions to enhance the learning experience.

4. Offers students and readers an up-to-date critical review of Best Practice Methods for the practice area focused on in each book. The final chapter of each book will guide readers through the professional literature and evidence-based research to provide an extensive review of current practice trends in the field of study.

As former practitioners, we chose the cases to be featured carefully. Each case making the "cut" focuses on the process (thinking, planning, and decision making) of practice and not necessarily on techniques or outcome. We chose cases based on one simple criterion: did it provide the best possible opportunity for excellence in practice education? We asked authors to "teach practice" by considering cases that were interesting and difficult, regardless of outcome, and to let readers into their internal thought processes as their case progressed.

In addition, each case focuses on client engagement and cultural responsiveness as important aspects of the practice process. As we like to remind our social work students, there are two words in the title of the profession: *social* and *work*. For the "work" to occur, students must learn to master the "social"—primarily, client engagement and relationship building in a culturally inviting and responsive manner.

As you will learn in Chapter 1, clinical practice is relationship based and, from our perspective, relies more on the processes involved in relationship building and client engagement than technical intervention skills. Successful practice is often rooted more in the ability of practitioners to develop open and trusting relationships with client(s) than on their ability to employ specific methods of intervention.

Yet, this critically important element of practice is often ignored or only mentioned in passing as a given. Our experience with students, employees, and practitioner/trainees over nearly four decades suggests it is wrong to assume students and/or practitioners have competent engagement or relationship-building skills. Developing a professional relationship based in trust and openness, where clients feel safe to dialogue about the most intimate and sometimes embarrassing events in their lives, is the primary responsibility of the practitioner. Hence, each case presentation tries to provide a sense of this difficult and often elusive process, along with ways each author managed the emerging client relationship.

## TARGET AUDIENCE

We believe this series is applicable and useful for education and training programs from community college, to advanced undergraduate, and graduate programs in the helping professions. We also know of many social agencies that provide our previous texts to new employees for review and practice. Hence, the Casebooks are appropriate in social work, counseling psychology, counseling, mental health, psychology, and specialty disciplines such as marriage and family therapy, substance abuse, and mental health degree or certificate programs. Any educational or training program designed to prepare students to work with clients in a helping capacity may find the Casebooks useful as a learning tool.

## STRUCTURE OF CASES

In Chapters 2, 3, and 4, each case is presented as an in-depth narrative written as a story. The authors provide an inside look into actual therapy sessions as they build rapport, develop client engagement, and make decisions about how best to gather personal information leading to an accurate assessment, diagnoses, and treatment plan. These stories often include client-practitioner dialogue to help readers gaze inside a confidential therapy session and periodically explore practice literature to explain certain dilemmas as they arise in the case.

The narrative case studies are designed to maximize critical thinking, the use of professional literature, evidenced-based practice knowledge, and classroom discussion in the learning process. At various points throughout each case, the editors include a series of thought-provoking and/or action-based questions to guide and enhance the learning process. We want readers to collect evidence on different sides of an issue, evaluate that evidence, and develop a professional position they can defend in writing and/or discussion with other students in the classroom or seminar setting.

At the end of each case, readers can develop a comprehensive narrative assessment based on the client's information, accurate clinical diagnoses, appropriate treatment plan, and an emergency/safety plan. Moreover, readers are asked to determine the client's stage of change (see Chapter 1) for each diagnosis. Cases in this format make for excellent in-class exercises that teach both clinical decision making and professional assessment writing.

We hope that you find the cases and our formats as instructive and helpful in your courses as we have in ours. We have field tested these two formats in our courses, finding that students respond well to the length, depth, and rigor of the case presentations.

## ORGANIZATION OF THIS TEXT

We organized this book on Practice in Child and Family Welfare to maximize its utility in any course. Chapter 1 provides an overview of our Advanced Multiple Systems (AMS) practice approach, focusing on a series of Guiding Practice Principles gleaned from the editors' nearly 75 years of combined professional experience. The AMS is one potential organizing tool for students to use while reading and evaluating the cases.

The Guiding Practice Principles provide important ways of thinking and approaching clients in all practice settings to help the engagement, assessment, and treatment process. These principles are not connected to theory, method, or practice setting/role. Like a professional code of ethics, the Guiding Practice Principles offer critical elements for effective clinical and relationship decisions.

In Chapter 2, a case entitled **Child Protective Services**, we follow a Children's Protective Services Worker managing multiple cases, investigating abuse and neglect, and dealing with the challenges of assessing if children should be removed from their biological parents and placed in foster care.

In Chapter 3, **The Adoption of Curtis and William**, we follow the journey of two boys moving through the foster care system, the different systems they had to interact with, and how the adoption process works.

In Chapter 4, a case entitled **Inside My Head: The First 24 Hours, A Residential Placement**, we follow a teenage girl in residential foster care, along with her younger brother, waiting to see if the agency could place them together in an adoptive home. The key to this case is most of the information you will gather comes from the teenager's thoughts. It is a rare opportunity to read what a client is thinking and how they manage the world around them.

In Chapter 5, author Jessica R. Campbell shares her case, **A College Experience**, about a teenager who grew up in foster care while still connected to her biological family, now attending college. We learn the challenges she faces in college and the program created to support college students who experienced foster care.

In the final chapter, the author provides a comprehensive review of best practice methods in Child and Family Welfare.

## ACKNOWLEDGMENTS

We would like to thank the contributors to this text for their hard work, experience, and willingness to share their work with our audience. We would also like to thank Amy Smith, Alia Bales, Laura Pasquale, and all the professionals at Cognella for being great to work with, for their faith in the Casebook Series for the Human Services, and in our ability to manage multiple manuscripts at once. Additionally, we want to thank our students over the years for serving as "guinea pigs" as we refined our case formats for publication. Their willingness to provide honest feedback contributes mightily to this series.

Jerry L. Johnson: I want to thank my wife, Cheryl, for her support and willingness to give me the time and encouragement to write and edit. I also thank my equine herd—Joey, Hope, Zelda, Ruby, Pip, Rome, Bray, Tommy, Mister Mule, Hershey, Maddy, and Oprah—for helping provide peace in my life.

George Grant, Jr.: I want to thank my parents, Mr. George Grant, Sr. and Mrs. Dorothy Grant, for their love, commitment, and lessons of caring, compassion, and sharing your talents with others.

## REFERENCE

Johnson, J. L., & Grant Jr., G. (2005). *Casebook: Substance abuse*. Allyn & Bacon.

# CHAPTER 1

# A Multiple Systems Approach to Practice in Child Welfare

*Jerry L. Johnson & George Grant, Jr.*

IN THIS TEXT, we help readers build practice knowledge, values, and skills to work with clients, policy makers, and organizations in the child and family welfare system. We define child and family welfare with a starting point of child abuse and neglect. At least one child is connected to the child welfare system, which includes child protective services, foster care, and adoption, along with placement options for the protection of children, and county, state, and federal agencies, court systems, and public and private agencies that provide services for children and families in the child welfare system. The cases will explore multiple parts of the child welfare system shared by professionals sharing their stories of the challenges, pitfalls, and successes from working in one of the most complex systems in the United States. There is no one model for working with families. While there are definitions of child abuse and neglect, people can see the same interaction and one would define it as abuse and another would not. From judges, prosecutors, and law enforcement, there is no one way to define abuse and neglect, and when children should be placed in foster care or remain in their biological home. These are but a few examples of the challenges of working in this field and the stress it places on everyone to make the correct decisions.

The cases in this book attempt to tackle those challenges, discuss some of the complications, and demonstrate how systems can work together or clash with each other. Sometimes the systems can work together, but other times those conflicts are based on principles where people would feel like they are compromising their values. These principle-based positions mean there is no room for compromise. As you put yourself in the cases, assess the principled values on which you would not compromise and the impact it would have on clients and systems.

In this text, we provide a rare opportunity to study the processes and strategies involved working in the child welfare system taken from the caseloads of experienced practitioners. We include four cases, each written with deep and rich case detail designed to plunge readers into the thinking, planning, and approaches of the practitioners/authors. We challenge you to study their ideology and methods, to understand their clinical decision making, and then think critically using your background and experience to discover and propose alternative ways of working with the same clients. In other words, what would you do if you were the primary practitioner responsible for these cases? How would you approach the cases similarly or differently, and what are your reasons for these differences?

Before diving into the cases, this chapter introduces the Advanced Multiple Systems (AMS) practice perspective, along with the Guiding Practice Principles underlying the AMS. We include AMS and its principles for three reasons. First, AMS can be a guide to help assess and analyze the cases in this text. Each case chapter will ask you to complete a multiple systems assessment, diagnoses, treatment, and intervention plan. AMS provides a theoretical and practical approach for these exercises. Second, we hope you find that AMS makes conceptualizing cases clearer in your practice environment. Third, AMS and the practice principles offer an experience-based way of thinking and acting about and with clients across the practice spectrum. The Guiding Practice Principles offer young and experienced practitioners alike a time-tested way to think about and approach clients in clinical and other practice settings, and they provide the foundation on which successful practice rests.

We do not believe AMS is the only way—or necessarily even the best way—for all practitioners to think about clients. We know, through experience, that AMS and the Guiding Practice Principles are an effective way to think about practice with clients from diverse backgrounds and with different needs. While there are many approaches to practice, AMS offers an effective way to place clinical decisions in the context of client lives and experiences, giving engagement and treatment a chance to be productive.

## ADVANCED MULTIPLE SYSTEMS (AMS) PRACTICE

### Sociological Roots

> Whether the point of interest is a high power state or a minor literary mood, a family, a prison, and a creed—these are the kinds of questions the best social analysts have asked. They are the intellectual pivots of classic studies of (person) in society—and they are the questions inevitably raised by any mind possessing the sociological imagination. For that imagination is the capacity to shift from one perspective to another—from the political to the psychological;

from an examination of a single-family to comparative assessment of the national budgets of the world; from the theological school to the military establishment; from considerations of an oil industry to studies of contemporary poetry. It is the capacity to range from the most impersonal and remote transformations to the most intimate features of the human self—and see the relations between the two. Back of its use is always the urge to know the social and historical meaning of the individual in the society and in the period in which he (or she) has his quality and his (or her) being. (Mills, 1959, p. 7; parentheses added)

Above, sociologist C. Wright Mills provided a critical description of the sociological imagination. As it turns out, Mills's sociological imagination is also an apt description of AMS. Mills believed that linking people's "private troubles" to "public issues" (p. 2) was the most effective way to understand people and their problems, by placing them in social and historical context. It forces investigators to contextualize individuals and families in the framework of the broader social, political, economic, and historical environments in which they live. Ironically, this is also the goal of clinical practice (Germain & Gitterman, 1996; Longres, 2000). Going further, Mills (1959) states:

We have come to know that every individual lives, from one generation to the next, in some society; that he (or she) lives out a biography, and that he (or she) lives it out within some historical sequence. By the fact of his (or her) living he (or she) contributes, however minutely, to the shaping of this society and to the course of its history, even as he (or she) is made by society and by its historical push and shove. (p. 6)

Mills (1959) proposed this approach to help understand links between people, their lives, and the larger environment. Yet, while laying the theoretical groundwork for social research, Mills also provided the theoretical foundation for an effective approach to clinical practice. This suggests three relevant points directly related to clinical practice.

1. It is crucial to recognize the relationships between people's personal issues and strengths (private troubles) and the issues (political, economic, social, historical, and legal) and strengths of the multiple systems environment (public issues) in which people live. This includes recognizing and integrating issues and strengths at the micro (individual, family, extended kin, etc.), mezzo (local community), and macro (state, region, national, and international policy, laws, political, economic, and social) levels during client engagement, assessment, treatment, and aftercare.

2.  Understanding these relationships can lead people to change. We speak here about second-order change or a significant change that makes a long-term difference in people's lives, the kind of change that alters the fundamental rules of an existing system, helping people see themselves differently in relationship to their world. Second-order change is often forced from the outside of the system (or person). This level of change becomes possible when people make links across their world in a way that makes sense to them (Freire, 1993). In other words, clients become "empowered" to change when they understand their life in the context of their world, how often their lives have been limited or defined by that world, and realizing they have previously unknown or unimagined choices in how they live, think, feel, believe, and act.

3.  Any assessment, clinical diagnoses, or treatment plan excluding multiple systems links does not provide a holistic picture of people's lives, their troubles, and/or strengths. The opportunity for change lessens when client history is overlooked. A practitioner cannot learn too much about their clients, their lives, and their attitudes, beliefs, and values stemming from their local environment, the influence of important relationships, and their sense of hope for a better future.

## AMS OVERVIEW

First, we define the foundational concept, the multiple systems perspective. Understanding these ideas provides the foundation for a common language and idea of the concepts used throughout the remainder of this chapter.

### Multiple Systems Perspective

Generally, a systems approach emphasizes the connectedness between people and their problems to the complex interrelationships existing in their world (Timberlake, Farber, & Sabatino, 2002). To explain these connections, systems theory emphasizes three important concepts: wholeness, relationships, and homeostasis.

*Wholeness* refers to the way various parts or subsystems interact to form a whole. This idea asserts that systems cannot be understood or explained unless the connectedness of the subsystems to the whole is understood, the nature of the relationships within the system, and the roles people play within that system. In other words, the whole is greater than the sum of its parts. Moreover, systems theory also posits that change in one subsystem will affect change in the whole system.

*Relationship* refers to the patterns of interaction and overall structures existing within and between subsystems. The nature of these relationships is more important than the system itself. That is when trying to understand or explain a system (individual, family, organization, etc.), how subsystems connect through relationships, the characteristics of the relationships between subsystems, and how the subsystems interact provide clues to understanding the whole and the problems needing treatment.

Hence, the application of systems theory is primarily based on understanding relationships. In systems (families, individuals, etc.), problems occur between people (relationships), not "in" them. Even individual diagnoses are looked at by how they affect self and others, along with how the symptoms and/or behavior is encouraged or maintained by relationships within the system. Hence, from this perspective, people's internal problems related to the nature of the relationships in the systems where they live and interact.

*Homeostasis* refers to the idea that systems strive to maintain and preserve the existing system, its rules and relationships, the status quo. For example, family members assume roles that serve to protect and maintain family stability, often at the expense of "needed" change or their health and well-being.

The natural tendency toward homeostasis in systems represents what we call the "dilemma of change," where a dilemma is a series of choices, none of which are good (Johnson, 2004). This is best described as the apparent conflict occurring when clients approach moments of significant change. People struggle with the dilemma of change: should they change, risking the unknown, or try remaining the same, even if the status quo is unhealthy or unproductive?

When individuals within systems change, it forces others within the system to change as well, even if only concerning the individual trying to change. So, if a mother with a long-term substance use disorder suddenly finds sobriety, her newfound life will require everyone else in the family to change concerning her, even if they do not want to change. This often starts a series of relationship reactions, sometimes leading to the reinstatement of homeostasis that could come in the form of the mother relapsing to ensure the family status quo.

What do we mean, then, by the term **multiple systems**? People (clients) are part of and interact with multiple systems simultaneously. These systems interact on many levels, ranging from the micro level (individual and families), the mezzo level (local community, institutions, organizations, the practitioner and their agency, etc.), to the macro level (culture, laws and policy, politics, oppression and discrimination, international events, etc.)—how these various systems come together and comprise the "whole" that is the client. The nature of these interactions and relationships often helps explain the nature of a client's problems.

In practice, the client (individual, couple, family, etc.) is not the "system," but one of many interacting subsystems in a maze of other subsystems constantly interacting to create the system—the client plus elements from multiple subsystems at each level. It would be a mistake to view the client as the whole system, or that individual problems are not affected by other aspects of the system (family and beyond).

This level of understanding—the system as the whole produced through multiple system interactions—is the primary unit of investigation for practice. As stated above, it is narrow to consider the client as a functioning independent system with peripheral involvement with others existing outside of their intimate world. These issues and relationships work together to help shape and mold the client who, in turn, shapes and molds their relationship to the other subsystems. Yet, the person-of-the-client is but one part of the system in question during interactions with people in positions of power.

For example, an African American teenage student may have every intention of being a top academic performer in his mostly white high school. During class one day, the teacher asks something of the student, leading him to question the teacher on her reasons for asking. In this young man's family and culture, it is not unusual to talk loudly, more loudly than what is often considered "normal" in a white environment.

The student's tone and volume encourage his white teacher to believe the student is being challenged or even threatening, depending on her subjective experience with students of color. The student is immediately sent to the principal's office for "acting out" and being "threatening," although he asked for clarification in the ways of his family and culture, not his teachers. This student then risks becoming labeled as "oppositional" among the other teachers, whom his teacher talks to every day. He also risks being referred for therapy or counseling to treat his "oppositional defiant disorder." In this case, multiple systems interacted against what our fictional student believed and was taught about his right to question and seek clarification about teacher requests. Interacting systems collided to create a problem where none existed.

AMS provides an organized framework for gathering, conceptualizing, and analyzing multiple system client data to help practitioners proceed with the helping process. Beginning with culturally responsive client engagement, a comprehensive multi-systems assessment points toward a holistically based treatment plan that requires practitioners to select and utilize appropriate practice theories, models, and methods—or combinations thereof—that best fit the client's unique circumstances and needs.

AMS is a perspective or framework for understanding clients. It relies on the practitioner's ability to use a variety of theories, models, and methods in their routine approach with clients. For example, an AMS practitioner will have the skills to apply different approaches to individual treatment (client-centered, cognitive-behavioral, etc.), family treatment (structural, narrative, Bowenian, etc.), work with couples, in groups, arrange for specialized care if needed, and as an advocate on behalf of their client.

Practitioners must also know how to determine, primarily through the early engagement and assessment process, which theory, model, or approach (direct or indirect, for example) would work best for each client. Hence, successful practice using AMS relies heavily on the practitioner's ability to engage and assess client problems and strengths competently. Practitioners develop a sense of their client's interaction and relationship style—especially related to how they relate to authority figures—when determining which approach would best suit their circumstance. For example, a reserved, quiet, or thoughtful client or someone who lacks assertiveness may not be well served by a direct, confrontational approach, regardless of the practitioner's preference. Elsewhere we provide a more detailed exploration of the AMS perspective (Johnson & Grant, 2006, 2007).

## DIMENSIONS OF AMS ASSESSMENT

To operationalize AMS from a client data collection and assessment perspective, below is a list, with brief explanations, of the dimensions of information needed. Collecting client information according to the following dimensions will provide the multiple systems data needed to develop a systemic understanding of each client.

### A. Dimension 1: Client Description, Presenting Problem, and Referral

Beyond a physical and demographic description of clients, it is important to understand, from the client's perspective, what is/are the problems leading to the first session. Do not focus only on the problems that referral sources claim, but learn the client's idea of the presenting problem. This may be anything from a recent arrest to a drinking problem, to wanting to curry favor with a judge, or to get their family off their back. Whatever the client says is the problem is the problem you must address first.

A good practitioner also should understand how a referral was made, when, and the reasons why. If it's a mandated referral (i.e., court, PO, etc.), it is helpful to discover the client's reaction to the referral. It is also essential to explore the events or circumstances that led to the referral at this moment in time.

### B. Dimension 2: Treatment/Therapy History

Include in this discussion any type of therapy, counseling, education, or more intensive treatments, inclusive of any problem. That is, explore past treatments for substance use, mental health, and others for the client and family members.

More than a place to record dates, locations, and lengths of stay, this conversation should be targeted at what clients "thought" about their experiences. What did they like and dislike about treatment, therapists, counselors, and/or programs, and their reasoning behind their beliefs? Also, ask new clients about their expectations of therapy and therapists. An experienced clinician can use this conversation to learn a lot about how best to engage new clients, based entirely on their report of past treatment experiences.

## C. Dimension 3: Substance Use History

Given the prevalence of co-occurring disorders across the practice spectrum, it is essential for practitioners to gather substance use information about their client and his/her/their family, regardless of the client's presenting problem and/or the specialty of the organization. In this discussion, focus on the age of first use of alcohol and other drugs for "recreation," substances used in the previous 30 days (including prescribed drugs), their favorite substances used in what combinations. Pay careful attention to the substances that clients mix, hoping to understand if the combination of substances can lead to an accidental overdose.

If there is evidence of regular and patterned substance use, it is also important to discover if clients (or their family members) have ever been diagnosed with a substance use disorder. Understanding the role substance use, as a co-occurring disorder, can have on other problems, experienced practitioners would not perform any assessment without having explored the possibility substance use issues exist.

## D. Dimension 4: Mental Health History

Data collected in this dimension focuses on symptoms, behaviors, thoughts, and feelings regarding both mental health functioning and potential mental health disorders. Practitioners can use one of the many mental health screening instruments available, including instruments designed to understand exposure to traumatic events and experiences. If there is evidence of trauma exposure, here is where practitioners explore the occurrence of events or activities leading to trauma reactions in clients. Explore past or present evidence of abuse and neglect (sexual, physical, emotional, domestic), exposure to violence, or being the victim of violence.

It is important to learn about suicidal thoughts and gestures in the past or present, tendencies toward violence against family, strangers, etc., and other kinds of physicality that can stem from issues of mental health. It is also important to help understand the connections, if any, to the reports of mental problems and their substance use history above.

## E. Dimension 5: Family History

Taking a family history helps place your client and his/her/their problems in the context of their family, defined as anybody your client considers "family." The most effective family history is one that comprises a look at three generations from the client presenting for therapy. Beyond the details of who is living, married, divorced, or deceased, explore the quality of relationships, problems across members and generations, and the level of support clients believe they receive from their families.

Experience teaches that problems tend to "run" in families, across subsystems and generations. A three-generation genogram with problems noted on the genogram provides clinicians with a quick and comprehensive look across the family that often helps explain your client in different ways. Practitioners cannot collect "too much" family history and background.

## F. Dimension 6: Social Support and Engagement

In this dimension, explore with clients their social connections and the value clients place on these connections. The overarching question to answer here is, "When your life hits the skids, whom do you call for support?" Clinicians look to assess the degree to which people are connected to their community in productive ways, or disconnected, isolated, and/or alone.

Explore with clients support group attendance, social clubs, friends, family, and other groups they may be involved in, now and in the past. If they have quit these connections, discover their reasons for quitting. Also include their membership at places of worship, military history, workplaces, and/or any other group of people whom your clients find supportive. Also, ask about your client's hobbies and what they like to do for fun. Have their interests narrowed over the years? Often, as problems become serious, people abandon activities, groups, and people, making their life narrow, losing the opportunity for positive social support (Johnson, 2004).

Do not ignore the supportive nature of engagements often deemed negative and counterproductive, like street gangs. These groups exist because they provide disaffected people with a sense of purpose, connection, structure, rules, and meaning. That is, street gangs and these groups exist largely because their members cannot or do not find these important and meaningful connections in their families and communities. Involvement in these groups demonstrates how important meaningful social connections are to people.

## G. Dimension 7: Culture

While we provide a more extensive discussion of culture in practice later as a Guiding Practice Principle, it is essential to inquire about the client's cultural values, beyond race, gender, ethnicity, sexual preferences, and faith traditions. Culture represents more than demographics. That is, how do your client's cultural values shape choices, behaviors, values, and meaning (Johnson, 2000)? Practitioners must be aware that one's culture presents a fertile area for relying on stereotypes and personal bias. Understanding a client's culture has more to do with the ability to gather personal information from diverse clients than on a basic understanding of larger cultural groups and their tendencies. We are not concerned about how "Mexican families" operate, but about how the Mexican family in your office, right in front of you, operates, and believes (Johnson, 2004).

## H. Dimension 8: Biopsychosocial Connection

Helping students understand the impact of the biopsychosocial connection in clinical practice can be difficult. Certainly, in addition to the external effects of multiple systems on people, there is also the person as a system to consider. After many years of trying different ways of explaining the biopsychosocial connection unsuccessfully, I heard the following explanation that makes the relationship clear.

For those readers sensitive to the use of the following analogy, I apologize. However, students have suggested this analogy makes the biopsychosocial interaction clear.

1. A person's biological dimension (including genetics) **loads the weapon;**
2. A person's psychology (personality, coping mechanisms, attitude, etc.) **aims the weapon;** and
3. A person's social environment (friends, family, support, etc.) **pulls the trigger.**

Again, I apologize for the use of weapons as an analogy in a text like this, but if you think about it, it provides an apt description of how these three dimensions work together. Ironically, treatment, especially with clients experiencing co-occurring disorders, often works in the opposite order. That is:

1. Help clients create a supportive and helpful social environment to stop problem behaviors, or to stop pulling the trigger (i.e., substance use, mental health symptoms, ignoring medications, fighting, etc.);
2. Once the behavior has changed or ceased (periods of sobriety, calm, fewer symptoms, etc.), we can begin working on the person's aim toward problems or psychology involved by teaching new coping skills, relapse prevention, anger management, etc., through therapy;
3. Our profession does not have the technology, other than perhaps through medication, to change people's biological or genetic makeup.

Staying with the above analogy, while it is not today possible to "unload the weapon," it is possible to help clients stop "pulling the trigger" on problematic behaviors through social support, long enough to work on the underlying issues in therapy to change how people "aim the weapon."

In addition, several elements comprise the biopsychosocial perspective. Longres (2000) identifies two dimensions of individual functioning, the biophysical and the psychological, subdividing the psychological into three subdimensions: the cognitive, affective, and behavioral. Elsewhere, we added the spiritual/existential dimension to this conception (Johnson & Grant, 2006). Understanding how the biological, psychological, spiritual and existential, and social environment interacts is instrumental in developing an appreciation of how their environment influences individuals' influence.

## GUIDING PRACTICE PRINCIPLES

AMS is based on several Guiding Practice-Tested Principles (GPP), derived from the current professional practice literature and the editors' 75-plus years of combined practice experience. The Guiding Practice Principles are the core—the guts, as it were—of the Advanced Multiple Systems (AMS) practice perspective.

Over the years, we have searched for the core of excellent practice. Hence, we developed the Guiding Practice Principles as the foundation of AMS as our way to approach this core. Here, Guiding Practice Principles (GPP) are defined as those precepts, ideas, attitudes, and practices used to guide an ethical, receptive, respectful, welcoming, and competent approach to clients and client problems regardless of the specific issues, culture, worldview, professional theories, models or methods, professional disciplines, or practice settings. GPP describes fundamental ways of thinking and acting by human service professionals that, if consistent, transcend theory, model, or method. GPP is not tied to practice theory, model, or method; not bound by practitioner and client culture, practices, and beliefs. Practitioners may use any intervention or treatment choice to match their client's culture or background specifically if that choice is deemed ethical and not in violation of one or more of the Guiding Practice Principles.

Like a professional code of ethics, the GPP are guidelines for thinking and decision making. GPP rarely describes specific rules or actions, but the larger goals of professional human interaction and relationship. Accordingly, as a practitioner, you can utilize whatever best practice or evidence-based theory and/or method deemed appropriate to help clients. GPP provides a helpful filter for practice decision making.

## GUIDING PRACTICE PRINCIPLES EXPLAINED

### First Principle (Umbrella Principle): Healthy Outcomes (and Lives) are Directly Related to People's Connections to Helpful, Supportive Systems, Across a Lifetime

The First Principle is universal ... it applies to everyone. That is, everyone who is either seeking a better life through therapy, counseling, and/or recovery or who lives a well-adjusted, healthy, and happy life abides at some level to the First Principle. Healthy people maintain lifelong, positive, and invariably intimate connections with helpful, healthy, and supportive systems throughout life.

We define helpful and supportive systems as any person, people, group, organization, program, etc., a person finds helpful and supportive; has the person's best interests at heart; and is one in which the person feels positively engaged. While the specifics and the nature of helpful and supportive systems change across a lifetime, the value of these connections is difficult to question (Johnson, 2004). They are the foundation of personal resilience. These relationships are the "difference that makes a difference" in treatment, recovery, life, and happiness.

Helpful and supportive systems also include counselors, therapists, and human service programs. But it is so much more in real life. Most people's "helpful and supportive systems" include everything from close friends and relatives to social clubs and groups, leagues, places of worship, coffee friends, support groups, etc. More importantly, a system is only helpful and supportive to the extent clients believe it is and **are willing to use it.**

It is not enough to say clients have "access" to helpful and supportive systems. We all have access to helpful and supportive systems. It does not matter that helpful and supportive systems are available—they are everywhere, personal, and professional. It only matters if a person is willing to seek and accept help and support from said system. Without personal investment and belief in its value as support, it is not helpful and supportive.

For example, it is only a partial step to give a client a list of Alcoholics Anonymous (AA) or Narcotics Anonymous (NA) meetings in the local area. Working to satisfy the tenets of the First Principle also includes discussing with clients what the organization is about, the reasons why it may be important for them to attend, the reasons why making friends and/or finding a sponsor are important. Based on your knowledge of the client, discussing with them before they attend what parts of the meetings your specific client may find difficult or objectionable is a way of removing excuses for not attending.

Why all this effort? Because we know attendance alone, without steps toward engagement in the process, will not provide long-term help and support. If you've heard the saying that people can be "lonely in a crowded stadium," then the importance of this discussion should be clear. One cannot be lonely in a crowded stadium or an AA/NA meeting if they are engaged with others and talking to people. To repeat—engagement, not access, is the key to successful social support in the First Practice Principle.

Hence, the First Practice Principle is the umbrella under which all else in professional practice falls. It is so important to understand and fundamental to long-term life success, and the **Final Practice Principle states: When all else fails, never do anything with and/or to a client that violates the First Principle.** Successful practitioners approach every client situation with the First Principle in mind, whether they know the specific definition or not.

What does this mean in practice? Those abiding by the First Practice Principle believe no matter how much or how little progress clients make, how resistant or unmotivated they may appear, or whether they do anything at all toward changing while in our care, they ensure clients do not leave their professional relationship angry, insulted, disillusioned, negatively labeled; or hostile toward help, helpers, and/or helping systems. At the very least, abiding by the First Practice Principle means helping set clients up for future success by not driving them away from care and/or helpers out of personal or professional frustration at the client's lack of engagement, motivation, or change.

The First Practice Principle requires both short- and long-term thinking. Is anything happening in therapy, or am I, as the practitioner, acting in such a way with my client today that may damage or make less likely he/she/they will be open to engaging with helpers and/or helping systems later in life when they might be more ready to change? In other words, how one is treated today will impact them in many important ways later. The First Practice Principle requires helpers to do everything within their power to ensure said impact is positive.

While we discuss client motivation later, it is important to understand the developmental nature of change and people's willingness to effect it. That is, people progress through different developmental stages related to the depth and severity of their problems, acceptance of their problems, the need for change, the motivation to change, and the courage and willingness to embark on a difficult and sometimes painful process called change (Johnson, 2004). Some make it; some do well and disappear, finding success through other services or support; some do well in the short term only to fade away; and, unfortunately, some never make progress and/or regress.

Often, when client progress lags, stalls, or never begins, often out of frustration, therapists directly and personally confront clients about their lack of progress, engagement, or motivation with rude, accusatory, or even personally hostile remarks (Johnson & Grant, 2005).

The epitome of frustration occurs when therapists or counselors talk to clients, beginning with the phrase, "What you need to do is ..." When I hear students or practitioners talking to clients in this way, I ask them, "Who in your life has the right to talk to you in that way?" Rarely do they have an answer. This approach is usually born out of the practitioner's need to control or be paternalistic, thinking of troubled clients more as children than struggling people.

In the substance use field, programs and practitioners often expel clients from treatment because they are not "ready" for change or because they experienced a relapse. At this moment, as you read this, all over the substance use treatment world clients are being dismissed from treatment for lack of progress; sent back out to drink and/or use drugs, risking arrest, injury, death, or the death of others so they can "hit bottom" and prove to the program they are "bad enough" or "desperate enough" to deserve help. The net result of these frustration-born tactics is to drive clients away from you, your agency, and perhaps the helping profession in the future. Why would someone ever want to seek therapy again after being treated in these ways? They probably would not.

In service of the First Practice Principle, our job is to ensure, as much as possible, when clients fade away from treatment or never get started at all, they do so based on personal choice and not because we "drove" them away through unusual behavioral expectations, attitude, inappropriate professional labels, misguided confrontation, attempts at control, and/or our professional or personal frustrations at their lack of progress.

Given the First Principle requirement of lifelong connections, it is good for practitioners to realize they are only a small part of the larger network of possible helpful systems a person needs during their lifetime. Unfortunately, we in the helping professions often see ourselves as far more, sometimes to the detriment of clients needing to establish their own networks.

Yet, while our professional role(s) is often short on the time line of lifelong connections, it can be the most important step in the process if we see to it clients make, foster, and utilize these connections during and after their time with us. That is, professional helpers play a seminal role in First Practice Principle work, largely because we become a client's initial "helpful" system. We are often the gatekeeper for help and lifelong change. How we interact with and treat people at perhaps the most vulnerable moment in their lives often determines the extent to which they will want to pursue other helpful systems in their lives in the future.

Hence, if we learn to treat even the most reluctant, angry, or resistant client with dignity, respect, and compassion, it is possible they may readily engage with us later, their next therapist or program, and/or find helpful and supportive systems in their communities. Not because the next therapist or program is necessarily "better" or "more skilled," but because your relationship formed the groundwork for clients to move developmentally closer to being ready for the excruciating work of changing their lives. Working to abide by the First Practice Principle may be more important in the long run than it is in terms of positive short-term, therapeutic outcomes. The First Principle is for life, not short-term gain.

The First Practice Principle consists of two important elements, each speaking to different aspects of the Principle. Indeed, it speaks to the importance of client engagement and the value of hope in people's lives.

## Client Engagement

Fundamental to the First Practice Principle is the ability to rapidly develop rapport leading to client engagement. In this text, client engagement

> ... occurs when you develop a trusting and open professional relationship that promotes hope and presents viable prospects for change. Successful engagement occurs when you create a social context in which vulnerable people (who often hold jaded attitudes toward helping professionals) can share their innermost feelings, as well as [their] most embarrassing and shameful behavior with you, a total stranger, over a relatively short period. (Johnson, 2004, p. 93)

Successful practice, regardless of setting or problems, is built on the foundation of trusting, respectful, and emotionally intimate relationships with their clients (Johnson, 2004). Clinical models and/or interventions are not effective without successful client engagement. Clients have no reason to accept help at a personal level from a therapist if they do not first like, and then come to trust and respect, them.

For example, I ask students to ponder how vulnerable, truthful, and motivated they would be with a therapist they did not like or come to trust and respect; would they accept help from anyone they did not trust or who did not treat them with dignity and respect? This is fundamental human relationship dynamics. To new clients, we are total strangers. They have no reason to trust or respect us when we meet. Simply having a college degree or an office with a "shingle" or because a judge ordered them to see us does not change basic, fundamental human relationship dynamics.

Becoming skilled in the nuances of successful client engagement is based on the fundamentals of being genuine, available, and focused on their clients. Most importantly, it is based on being friendly, open, welcoming, and polite, exhibiting these behaviors even when clients are hostile, angry, and resistant. When practitioners are nice and friendly, clients are not angry with them personally, but their circumstances led them to therapy.

Successful client engagement comes through understanding and accepting people's perceptions of their reality and not the "objective" reality of the practitioner. Seeking to understand how people perceive their world, problems, and the people around them increases the likelihood they will feel understood. This approach contributes to a professional relationship based on the client's life and belief systems, is consistent with their worldview, and one that is culturally appropriate.

In short, understanding people's perceptions leads practitioners to understand each client's definition of "common sense." It is important to remember that "common sense" is only common and sensible to one person. There is no general definition of common sense. Common sense does not exist outside of people's social, environmental, family, and cultural contexts. It is unique to every person, depending on where they live and come from.

Being mindful of the definitions people learn from their culture underlies not only what they do but also what they perceive, feel, and think. This knowledge places practitioners on the correct path to "start where the client is." It emphasizes the cultural uniqueness of each client and the need to understand each client in their context and belief systems, not the practitioner's context or belief systems.

Different people attribute a different meaning to the same events, even within the same family or community. One cannot assume people raised in the same family will define their social world similarly. For example, the sound of gunfire in the middle of the night may be frightening or normal, depending upon where a person resides and what is routine and accepted in their specific environment. Moreover, simply because some members of a family are unfazed by nightly gunfire does not mean others in the same family will not be traumatized by it.

Additionally, people use language differently based on established or evolving cultural beliefs. For example, alcohol consumption is defined as problematic depending upon how the concept of "alcohol problem" is socially constructed in specific environments. Clients from so-called drinking cultures may define drinking six alcoholic drinks daily as normal, while someone from a different cultural background may see this level of consumption as problematic. I once worked in Russia and found an issue that demonstrates this point explicitly. Colleagues in Russia stated rather emphatically that consuming one "bottle" (approximately a US pint) of vodka per day was acceptable and normal. People consuming more than one bottle per day were defined as having a drinking problem. The normal, one-bottle-per-day level of consumption in the United States would be considered by most as clear evidence of problem drinking.

It is worth repeating: upholding the First Practice Principle requires the ability to engage clients in open and trusting professional relationships. The skills needed to engage clients from different backgrounds and with different personal and cultural histories are what drives practice, which determines the difference between successful and unsuccessful practice. Advanced client engagement skills allow the practitioner to elicit in-depth, personal information in a dialogue between client and practitioner (Johnson, 2004), providing the foundation for strengths-based client empowerment leading to change.

## Fostering, Building, or Rediscovering Hopes and Dreams

Early in my career, I learned a lesson so important it became a hallmark of my practice approach. It helps me effectively engage clients from all walks and ages, races, ethnicities, genders, with multiple problems; the motivated, unmotivated, mandated, and hostile alike. It centered my approach on client motivation, long before models and methods came along to help with this (which we will discuss later). What I learned is:

> *Clients do not seek help because of their problems. They seek help because they lost the hope of being able to solve their problems on their own (or in their social networks).*

Accordingly, helping professionals are not only in the problem-solving business but also in the "hope" business. What ... not in the problem-solving business? When someone comes to us because they drink too much, isn't it our job to get them to drink less ... or quit drinking? That's problem solving ... right?

Well, yes and no. Of course, as practitioners, we want to help people change by solving their problems. There is no doubt about this. This might be the reason most of us endeavor to join this profession in the first place, to help people with their problems. Yet, most clients, even those with significant levels of personal denial, already know they need to change something, even if they will not admit it. Often, they already know what must change; they simply are not ready to admit it to us, mainly because they are not ready to assume responsibility to change. If all we needed to do is encourage people to change and have them do it, this would be easy work. Unfortunately, that is not how it works.

Our success, or skill, is not telling someone who drinks too much they need to quit drinking. Almost anybody can figure that out. The real skill—or art—of practice is getting clients to act even when they initially do not want to change. That is, before solving problems, our main task is helping convince people, at the deepest level possible, that change is not only positive and desirable, but more importantly … possible.

First, an experienced practitioner helps clients discover, perhaps for the first time, that change is possible. When clients learn they too can change—that a better life is not just for "other people"—they can become motivated to solve problems in the short term and maintain short-term changes throughout their lifetime.

Problems get solved by models, methods, and interventions. However, here we speak of the groundwork needed before models, methods, and interventions can work. To accomplish this, we first discover people's sense of **hope**; hope for a better future, hope for change, and hope they can be effective change agents in their own lives. Here, hope is defined as a person's expectation for the possibility of a better tomorrow, a sense of the future that develops over time and is a function of interactions between people and their environments.

While there is little consensus in the professional literature about what hope is, whether it is innate to the human condition, and/or how it is experienced (Polgar, 2017; Snyder, 2002), all agree having hope provides a sense of optimism for the future. An optimism that leads people to believe the difficult and painful journey toward a better life might be worth it. That is, hope for better, hope for different, and/or hope that change is even possible … and good. A sense of hope, as defined here, is the foundation of motivation to change. With it, change is worth a try. Without it, why bother?

Of course, for many people, the prospect of hope for a better tomorrow is difficult, if not impossible, to imagine. Their lives and existence preclude them from having hope for anything except, perhaps, survival. Whether it be from poverty, pain, violence, trauma, discrimination/racism, war, or their overall social environment, we cannot assume our clients know what it means to have a sense of optimism for the future; they are often devoid of the ability to dream.

According to Polgar (2017), "Most, if not all, who avail themselves of social work services live under siege conditions" (p. 271). That is, most clients find themselves under such significant personal and environmental stress, perhaps feeling under attack by their world, they end up focusing only on existing. People living under siege seek survival. They are often unable to visualize or imagine a positive future or engage in the kind of reflection required to realize, develop, or enhance hope for their future. Hence, people living under environmental siege can, at best, experience hope as an expectation there may be a tomorrow, but certainly not a better one (Polgar, 2017).

Many people do not understand, or worse yet, cannot allow themselves to believe in the idea, that a better life is possible and attainable. Perhaps their circumstances disrupted the ability to hope and dream from the beginning, or it was stolen or extinguished at an early age and never restored. Without a sense of hope and the ability to dream, people will not undertake the effort to change their lives with the sense of determination and motivation often required.

Yet, the loss of hope is usually larger than an individual problem. It also suggests a loss of hope in the ability of their friends, family, and other support networks to help as well. As I say to my students and workshop audiences, a lack of problems is not what separates us from our clients. Usually, what separates us is the ability to call on people we trust and love when life gets difficult; people who will support, challenge, and comfort us. These support people will have our best interests at heart and help lead us away from difficulty toward something more positive. Many people coming for professional help do not have this buffer, what we believe constitutes resilience. In our practice, we define resilience as the quality of one's social support network and one's willingness to use it. The better the support network, the more resilient people become.

Moreover, it helps to understand that the process of asking for or accepting professional help defines in many ways people's lack of, or loss of, hope. For some, needing outside help in their lives is to admit they do not have "what it takes" to solve their problems. Asking outsiders to help can be an outright violation of their personal, family, or community cultural norms. That is, asking for help is akin to admitting failure or weakness and can lead to a sense of shame and humiliation. Without taking these issues—hope, humiliation, and cultural norms—as a starting point for practice, change will most likely not occur.

People come for services discouraged, sometimes lost, having either abandoned their hopes and dreams or never knowing hopes and dreams were possible. Understanding this is, in our view, the core of practice wisdom. That is, without hope, either rekindled or newly discovered, long-term change is out of reach. Without hope, the positive, healing, and powerful therapeutic relationship that leads to change becomes difficult. Hence, a respectful and trusting therapeutic relationship is more important in promoting positive clinical outcomes than specific therapeutic models or interventions (Johnson & Grant, 2005; Johnson, 2004).

## Principle A: Clients Are People, Too

The main point of this principle is simple, yet so often not practiced. "Clients are people, too" is not intended as being funny or cute, but serious. Practitioners who embody Principle A in their worldview and practice approach will find success with client engagement and relationship building. This principle is important, respectful, and offers clients a sense of dignity at what could be their most vulnerable moment. Principle A is an integral part of Principle B (Practice Privilege) discussed below, but it also makes sense on its own. The best way to earn a client's trust and respect is for practitioners to act in trustworthy and respectful ways. There is no other way to accomplish this feat. Therefore, Principle A: Clients Are People, Too, is defined as:

> *Practitioners should never expect their clients to act in ways the practitioner would not act in similar circumstances and under similar pressures. In fact, practitioners should never expect clients to act in ways practitioners do not act presently, in their private lives.*

I must ask, have you ever been late for an appointment or class when your lateness meant nothing more than you were late? You were not late because you were "resistant" to your instructor or acting out in some meaningful, subconscious way. You were late. Period. If so, then why in the helping profession do we put so much time and effort into defining why our clients are sometimes late for their appointments? Even if they are late to every session, perhaps given their life circumstances, it's a major accomplishment to get themselves to your office. Perhaps they do not have reliable transportation. I've had a client tell me that their "ride" wanted sexual favors in exchange for the ride and they refused, making them miss the session completely.

Are there times when lateness or absence is a sign of avoidance ... sure. But without an open discussion with your clients about it and simply jumping to the conclusion that they are late to make you mad, it means you do not think your "clients are people, too." Sometimes, people have good reasons to be late or miss a session that have nothing to do with the therapist or the session. It just did not work that day.

While the lateness example is oversimplified, it makes the point of this principle. People coming for therapy, by definition, have problems they cannot solve on their own (see First Principle above). Depending on their problems and circumstances, they may be under heavy pressure and stress from substance use, mental health challenges, children, divorce, poverty, lack of transportation, violence, abuse, neglect, etc. These are all serious issues that compromise people's ability to respond, process, follow through, and live up to a behavior contract or therapy plan as we think they should as motivated clients. Moreover, our client's lives can be toppled by what may seem to us middle-class therapists as the "smallest" things. We can claim "poor coping skills," but the fact remains our clients are often dealing with more than we will ever know or understand. Given the severity and difficulty of some clients' lives, it is a miracle of coping they can even get up in the morning, let alone make every session on time and fulfill a therapy contract from day to day.

When a client struggles to live up to our standards, first ask yourself the question: how would I respond under the same circumstances? This is called developing empathy. Have I ever not followed through on a work task? Have I ever been unfocused because of troubles in my personal life? Have I ever left my home a mess because I was too tired to clean it up? Have I ever been short-tempered with my partner, spouse, kids because of my stress and not because of them? Have I ever slept late, been late, skipped, taken a day off just because I felt like it instead of "being a responsible adult?"

If the answer is "yes" to any of these questions, then why is it "something deeper" when our clients do the same things? Give your clients the same benefit of the doubt we expect from others and ourselves, have empathy for people trying to navigate life. Discuss it with them, find out what happens to cause them not to follow through, and most of all, be open to cutting them some slack. After all, clients are people, too!

## Principle B: Check Your Practice/Professional Privilege at the Door

Social privilege is a special, unearned advantage or entitlement, used to one's benefit or the detriment of others; often, the groups that benefit from it are unaware of it. It provides unearned access to resources that are only available to some people because of their social group membership, with immunity granted to or enjoyed by one group above and beyond the common advantage of others (www.ncjj.org/what-privilege, 2019). The idea of identifying the social privileges of certain groups (i.e., rich, white males) is an important conversation related to inequities and social justice. Social privilege is bestowed upon certain groups in certain situations by the larger system of forces and history over many years, often to the detriment of everyone not in the privileged groups. Let us take a moment and explore how this occurs.

## Structural and Historical Systems of Privilege and Oppression: Who Holds the Power?

Often embedded in laws, policies, and social institutions are oppressive influences such as racism, sexism, homophobia, and classism, to name a few. These structural issues play a significant role in the lives of clients (through maltreatment, racism, and discrimination) and in clinical practice. How people are treated (or how they internalize the historical treatment of self, family, friends, and/or ancestors) shapes how they believe, think, and act in the present. Oppression, operationalized through privilege, affects how people perceive what others feel about them, how they view the world and their place in it, and how receptive they are to professional service providers. Therefore, culturally respectful and responsive practice must consider the impact of structural systems of oppression, social privilege, our practice privilege, and injustice on clients, their problems, strengths, and potential for change.

Oppression and privilege are by-products of socially constructed notions of power, privilege, control, and hierarchies of difference. As stated above, they are created and maintained by differences in power. Those who have power can force people to abide by the rules, standards, and actions the powerful deem worthwhile, mandatory, or acceptable. Those who hold power can enforce particular worldviews; deny equal access and opportunity to housing, employment, or health care; define right and wrong, normal and abnormal; and imprison, confine, and/or commit physical, emotional, or mental violence against the powerless (McLaren, 1995; Freire, 1993). Most importantly, power permits the holder to "set the very terms of power" (Appleby, 2001, p. 37). It defines the interaction between the oppressed and the oppressor and between the practitioner and client. In the practice world, we as professional practitioners hold the power ... we have the privilege to enforce in our world in the same ways as dominant groups in the larger world.

Social institutions and practices are developed and maintained by the dominant culture to meet its needs and maintain its power. Everything and everybody are judged and classified accordingly. Even when the majority culture develops programs or engages in helping activities, these efforts will not include measures that threaten the dominant group's position at the top of the social hierarchy (Freire, 1993). For example, Kozol (1991) writes eloquently about how public schools fail by design, while Freire (1993) writes about how state welfare and private charity provide short-term assistance while ensuring that there are not enough resources to lift people permanently out of poverty.

Oppression and/or privilege are neither academic nor theoretical considerations; they are not faded relics of a bygone era. Racism did not end with the civil rights movement, and sexism was not eradicated by the feminist movement. Understanding how systems of oppression work in people's lives is of paramount importance for every individual and family seeking professional help, including those who belong to the same race, gender, and class as the practitioner.

Systems of oppression ensure unequal access to resources for certain individuals, families, and communities. However, while all oppressed people are similar in that they lack the power to define their place in the social hierarchy, oppression based on race, gender, sexual orientation, class, and other social factors is expressed in a variety of ways. Learning about cultural nuances is important in client assessment, treatment planning, and treatment (Lum, 1999). According to Pinderhughes (1989), there is no such thing as culture-free service delivery. Cultural differences between clients and practitioners in terms of values, norms, beliefs, attitudes, lifestyles, and life opportunities affect every aspect of the practice.

While larger social inequities are often discussed in terms of privilege, rarely have the helping professions examined and interrogated how professional or "Practice Privilege" operates in the relationships between practitioners and clients, clients and helping organizations, and how practitioners mediate the existing systems of oppression between clients and the larger social control systems (courts, CPS, mental health, etc.).

In the wrong hands, clinical training and practice bring the potential to exercise Practice Privilege to the detriment of our clients. Our professional degrees, licenses, certifications, and roles bring the power to define, label, and diagnose. We have the power to influence court decisions, parental custody decisions, existing relationships, and people's well-being. We make recommendations, give advice, judge, and decide our clients' futures and possibilities for change. In the wrong hands, we can dominate and define people's lives and the lives of their children well into the future, if not forever. This is the power of Practice Privilege.

This power is bestowed by the state and society as ours because we are members of this profession. We earn the right to be in our professional roles through education and training, but we do not earn the right to use it to shape and dominate other people's lives; to determine normal from abnormal, right from wrong, or healthy from unhealthy.

This notion of Practice Privilege must be considered, processed, and discussed in professional circles, much like the larger issues of social privilege. One of the insidious and consistent hallmarks of privilege is the people who have it do not know it exists, or when they exert it on others. This is difficult enough in daily life but potentially harmful among professional practitioners.

Oblivious practitioners can wield Practice Privilege to the detriment of clients in professional practice without knowing it. Fighting one's privilege takes bringing the unknown to the fore, examining one's ideas and practices in a way that interrogates the extent to which our profession and our professionals wielding practice privilege that reinforce our client's place down the social hierarchy. Without a close, serious, and vulnerable exploration of our practices, much like we ask clients to do every day, we seriously cannot examine Practice Privilege, leaving us to blindly treat our clients in ways that reinforce their place and whose opinions and beliefs do not matter as much as those of the privileged few.

### Principle C: Culturally Respectful and Responsive Client Engagement

Earlier, we defined client engagement as a mutual process occurring between clients and practitioners in a professional context created by practitioners. In other words, creating the professional space and open atmosphere that allows engagement to flourish is the primary responsibility of the practitioner, not the client. Practitioners must have the skills and knowledge to adjust their approach toward specific clients and the client's cultural context and not vice versa. Clients do not adjust to us and our beliefs, values, and practices—we adjust to them. When that occurs, the foundation exists for client engagement. Relationships of this nature must be performed in a culturally welcoming and responsive manner. Yet, what does this mean?

Over the last two decades, social work and other helping professions have been concerned with cultural competence in practice (Fong, 2001). Beginning in the late 1970s the professional literature has been replete with ideas, definitions, and practice models designed to increase cultural awareness and promote culturally appropriate practice methods. Yet, despite the attention given to the issue, confusion remains about how to define and teach culturally competent practice.

As stated earlier, over the years, many different ideas and definitions of what constitutes culturally competent practice have developed, as indicated by the growth of the professional literature since the late 1970s. To date, focus has primarily been placed in two areas: (1) the need for practitioners to be aware of their own cultural beliefs, ideas, and identities leading to cultural sensitivity; and (2) learning factual and descriptive information about various ethnic and racial groups based mostly on group-level survey data and analyses. Fong (2001) suggests that culture is often considered "tangential" to individual functioning and not central to the client's functioning (p. 5).

To address this issue, Fong (2001) builds on Lum's (1999) culturally competent practice model that focuses on four areas: (1) cultural awareness; (2) knowledge acquisition; (3) skill development; and (4) inductive learning. Besides inductive learning, Lum's model places focus mainly on practitioners in perpetual self-awareness, gaining knowledge about cultures, and skill building. While these are important ideas for cultural competence, Fong (2001) calls for a shift in thinking and practice, "to provide a culturally competent service focused solely on the client rather than the social worker and what he or she brings to the awareness of ethnicity" (p. 5). Fong (2001) suggests an "extension" (p. 6) of Lum's model by turning the focus of each of the four elements away from the practitioner toward the client. For example, cultural awareness changes from a practitioner focus to "the social worker's understanding and the identification of the critical cultural values important to the client system and themselves" (p. 6). This change allows Fong (2001) to remain consistent with the stated definition of culturally competent practice, insisting that practitioners

> ... operating from an empowerment, strengths, and ecological framework, provide services, conduct assessments, and implement interventions that are reflective of the clients' cultural values and norms, congruent with their natural help-seeking behaviors, and inclusive of existing indigenous solutions. (p. 1)

While we agree with the idea that "to be culturally competent is to know the cultural values of the client system and to use them in planning and implementing services" (Fong, 2001, p. 6), we want to make this shift the main point of a culturally competent model of client engagement. That is, beyond what should or must occur, we believe that professional education and training must focus on the skills of culturally competent client engagement that are necessary to make this happen, a model that places the ability to gather individual client cultural information at the center of practice. We agree with Fong (2001) that having culturally sensitive or culturally aware practitioners is not nearly enough. Practitioner self-awareness and knowledge of different cultures do not constitute cultural competence. We strive to find a method for reaching this worthy goal.

Here, cultural competence does not mean practitioners will become competent in other people's cultures. This is not only impossible with limited exposure but to assume it is possible is evidence of out-of-control practice privilege discussed earlier. We do not learn a "special" set of skills allowing us to transcend history, time, and our own culture to rapidly become competent in some else's culture.

Here, the central issue revolves around practitioners participating in inductive learning and the skills of grounded theory. In other words, regardless of practitioner beliefs, awareness, or sensitivities, cultural competence comes with the ability to gather the information necessary to understand their client's cultural values and meanings and "ground" their theory of practice in the cultural context of their client. They develop a unique theory of human behavior based on the cultural beliefs and practices of each client. Culturally competent client engagement does not happen by assessing the extent to which client lives "fit" within existing theory and knowledge about reality, most of which is middle-class and Eurocentric at its core (Johnson, 2004). Cultural competence:

> ... begins with learning about different cultures, races, personal circumstances, and structural mechanisms of oppression. It occurs when practitioners master the interpersonal skills needed to move beyond general descriptions of a specific culture or race to learn specific individual, family, group, or community interpretations of culture, ethnicity, and race. The culturally competent practitioner knows that within each culture are individually interpreted and practiced thoughts, beliefs, and behaviors that may or may not be consistent with group-level information. That is, there is tremendous diversity within groups, as well as between them. Individuals are unique unto themselves, not simply interchangeable members of a specific culture, ethnicity, or race who naturally abide by the group-level norms often taught on graduate and undergraduate courses on human diversity. (Johnson, 2004, p. 105)

Culturally competent client engagement revolves around the practitioner's ability to create a relationship, through the professional use of self, based in true dialogue (Freire, 1993; Johnson, 2004). We define dialogue as "a joint endeavor, developed between people (in this case, practitioner, and client) that move clients from their current state of hopelessness to a more hopeful, motivated position in their world (Johnson, 2004, p. 97). Elsewhere (Johnson, 2004), we detailed a model of culturally competent engagement based on Freire's (1993) definitions of oppression, communication, dialogue, practitioner self-work, and the ability to exhibit worldview respect, hope, humility, trust, and empathy.

To investigate culture in a competent manner is to take a comprehensive look into people's worldview—to discover what they believe about the world and their place in it. It goes beyond race and ethnicity (although these are important issues) into how culture determines thoughts, feelings, and behaviors in daily life. This includes what culture says about people's problems, culturally appropriate strengths and resources, the impact of gender on these issues, and what it means to seek professional help (Leigh, 1998).

The larger questions to be answered are how clients uniquely and individually interpret their culture; how their beliefs, attitudes, and behaviors are shaped by that interpretation; and how these cultural beliefs and practices affect daily life and determine lifestyle in the context of the larger community. Additionally, based on their cultural membership, beliefs, and practices, practitioners need to discover the potential and real barriers faced by clients in the world. For many clients of color and other minority groups, their worlds are defined by the racism, sexism, homophobia, and ethnocentrism that enforce limitations and barriers that others do not face.

What is the value of culturally competent client engagement? Helping clients discuss their attitudes, beliefs, and behaviors in the context of their culture—including their religious or spiritual belief systems—offers valuable information about their worldview, sense of social and spiritual connection, and/or practical involvement in their social world. Moreover, establishing connections between their unique interpretation of their culture and their daily life provides vital clues about people's belief systems, attitudes, expectations (social construction of reality), and explanation of behaviors that cannot be understood outside the context of their socially constructed interpretation of culture.

## Principle D: Motivation Matters

Earlier, we discussed the importance of assessing a client's hopes and dreams for a better future as setting the stage for change. This, along with building a trusting, respectful, and culturally appropriate therapeutic relationship, all serves to enhance and bolster the client's motivation to change. Without the proper motivation, comprised of all we have discussed to this point, clients will continue to lack progress and/or success in therapy.

> *Remember our core belief: Clients do not change because of models, methods, or interventions alone. They change because they are helped into a trusting and respectful therapeutic relationship based on enhancing their dignity as human beings, have hope they can change for the*

*better, and the motivation to endure the process of change. All of this is accomplished in the context of helpful and supportive systems of support to build personal resilience.*

Here, we look at ways to accurately assess your client's motivation for change. Miller and Rollnick (2002) suggest that clients with different stages of motivation, or change, require helpers to approach them differently, depending on the needs of their current stage of change and the needs to progress from earlier to later stages along the motivation continuum. The authors further state that "problems of clients being unmotivated or resistant occur when a counselor is using strategies inappropriate for a client's current stage of change" (Miller & Rollnick, 2002, p. 16).

In the 1980s, Prochaska and DiClemente (1982, 1984, 1986; DiClemente & Prochaska, 1985) developed the trans-theoretical model, commonly known as the Stages of Change model, based on their work with people trying to quit smoking. This model is based on how and why clients—either alone or with help—succeed at changing their addictive behavior. Subsequently, the Stages of Change Model has been adapted for other addictive behaviors such as food and alcohol and other drugs (Connors, Donovan, & DiClemente, 2001; DiClemente & Hughes, 1990; DiClemente, 1991). Previously, we expanded the stages of change to include mental health disorders, trauma disorders, and other disorders (Johnson, 2004).

There are six stages of change to be assessed during an assessment and treatment process. It is important to note, however, that the stages are fluid, meaning clients move from one to another, often needing between four and six "trips" through the stages before discovering long-term change (Miller & Rollnick, 1991). The stages of change are 1) Precontemplation; 2) Contemplation; 3) Preparation; 4) Action; 5) Maintenance; and 6) Relapse. The client's stage of change is assessed and determined for each diagnosable and treatable problem during each session. That is, if your client has two diagnosed co-occurring disorders (substance use and mental health), they are assessed along the stage of change continuum for each problem, during each session. These are described, along with assessment indicators, below.

## 1. Precontemplation

In the precontemplation stage, people have not yet considered the possibility they have a problem(s) or refuse to consider the possibility they may have a problem(s). Most often, clients in the precontemplation stage present with what appears as classic denial. These clients are often labeled resistant, recalcitrant, unmotivated, or not ready for treatment. They often refuse or make it difficult to perform an assessment, because they either have not considered their behavior as problematic or refuse to entertain a discussion about it. These clients are often mandated by outside systems, including the legal system, employers, or their families, but not always. Rarely will people in the precontemplation stage voluntarily submit themselves for treatment of any kind.

DiClemente (1991) suggests four subtypes of clients in the precontemplation stage. Called the "four R's" (DiClemente, 1991, p. 192), they include reluctance, rebellion, resignation, and rationalizing pre-contemplating clients.

Certain clients will fit the category of **reluctant pre-contemplators**. People in this category genuinely do not know or understand they have a problem(s) or even need to consider changing. These individuals are not as resistant as they are reluctant. Clients in this category will appear genuinely surprised, baffled, or taken aback by the suggestion they may have issues of any kind. They will appear as if they have never considered the possibility despite problematic behavior and significant negative life consequences. These clients require education and connections; problems and negative life consequences to their substance use and/or mental health disorders.

The **rebellious pre-contemplator** is resistant—resistant to being told what to do, to have their problems pointed out to them, and to most anything you do, except agree with them. If clients argue with nearly every question, refuse to respond or respond only in a hostile manner, and/or exhibit other oppositional behavior, it is quite possible you have a rebellious pre-contemplator in your presence. The best way to approach these individuals is to offer choices and/or to give the appearance you are not trying to change them or "telling them what to do."

**Resigned pre-contemplators** have usually given up on the prospect of change and appear overwhelmed by their problems. Often, these individuals will want to tell you how many times they have tried and failed to quit, how nothing seems to work, and/or how they may be "destined" to be a drug addict. These clients lack hope. Throughout your conversation, they make it known it is too late for them.

Finally, **rationalizing pre-contemplators** have "all the answers" (p. 193). These individuals do not consider the possibility of change because they "have it all figured out." They know someone who has bigger problems, have plenty of reasons why their problem is not a problem, or believe they would be fine if people would leave them alone. Rationalizing pre-contemplators can sound a lot like rebellious pre-contemplators, with one exception: the rationalizing pre-contemplators will be intellectual, while rebellious pre-contemplators will be angry and emotional. If you begin to feel like you are in an intellectual debate with your client about the extent of their problems, she, he, or they are probably a rationalizing pre-contemplator. These clients need to be approached as such, asking them to explain how they came to their conclusions. Contradictions between what is said and what is happening in their lives must be pointed out and clarified.

## 2. Contemplation Stage

The contemplation stage is characterized by ambivalence (Miller & Rollnick, 2002). Clients in this stage are open to the possibility they have problems to work on and change may be needed. However, they have not yet decided to change and appear hesitant to commit. This is a critical stage to recognize and one that can be quite frustrating, especially when you misread your client and act as if they are ready to change immediately. Miscalculations of this type often drive clients away or back into the precontemplation stage.

Clients in this stage will often state they know they should change and understand they have problems. They will give several reasons why they "should" change, but do not. The major difference is people in the contemplation stage acknowledge a vague problem exists and something "should" be done about it. To facilitate this ambivalence into a productive relationship, help clients explore past treatment failures, their fears about changing and staying the same, and offer hope that they can succeed. Clients in this stage, according to DiClemente (1991), lack a sense of self-efficacy needed to commit to a life-changing process. In this case, not only is it our job to assess this stage but to enhance it by employing approaches to help clients believe they have "what it takes" to succeed.

## 3. Preparation Stage

Clients in the preparation stage are already in the process of deciding to "stop a problem behavior or to initiate a positive behavior" (DiClemente, 1991, p. 197). These individuals have made a concrete decision to change. These are highly motivated individuals, ready to make a serious effort toward change. Clients in the preparation stage normally have already begun making changes or recently tried to change. They bring a serious commitment to their situation unseen in earlier stages. Your challenge is to enhance their motivation, offer support and linkages to resources needed to further their chances of success, and to discuss with them the potential barriers to change that may have to be confronted along the way. Helping clients through this anxiety and normal hesitation is critically important during this stage.

People in the preparation stage worry less about jargon and more about what to do. How can you tell the difference between clients in the preparation stage and those who are not? Listen for reports about previous action, concrete plan development, and whether they have reasons for why they cannot begin the process immediately. In the context of the dilemma of change, people in the preparation stage will have misgivings, hesitancies, and fears about what they are trying to accomplish. They will not usually be adamant about the need to change, nor will they dismiss the notion that change is difficult and frightening. Therefore, if clients are adamant about the need to change and unwilling to address the dilemma of change, it is likely they have not reached this stage.

## 4. Action Stage

People assessed to be in the action stage are committed to a course of action toward change (good or not). They have passed the point of decision making and are taking steps to change their life, perhaps attending therapy, support groups, changing their environment, and building supportive relationships. If clients in the determination stage commit to and begin a plan of action (DiClemente, 1991; Prochaska & DiClemente, 1982, 1984, 1986), they move from that stage to the action stage. Hence, the action stage is characterized by your client implementing their plan.

## 5. Maintenance Stage

Occasionally clients will present in the maintenance stage, primarily for support. However, many of these clients find the support they need in community support groups (AA or NA), in their churches, synagogues, or mosques, or among family and friends in the community. The maintenance phase is the last stage of successful change. Over time, clients slowly replace old ineffective behaviors with new patterns. As the new behavior patterns, attitudes, and beliefs become firmly entrenched, old patterns dissipate. However, it is important to note that this takes time, perhaps years to accomplish. Clients who submit themselves for assessment at this point are usually trying to avoid and prevent a relapse, discussed next.

## 6. Relapse Stage

This is another stage where you will often find clients coming for assistance. They have cycled through the stages, often more than once, and achieved a period of maintenance through action. However, in any treatment, relapse is a common and normal occurrence (Denning, 2000). For one reason or another, people often slip back into behaviors as they try to solidify their hold on their new lifestyle. These clients often come for assistance just after relapsing, with a weakened self-efficacy, guilt feelings, and a sense of resignation. The indicators of someone in the relapse stage are obvious. These are people who have been changing for any period who want to prevent a full-fledged relapse while continuing to make progress.

It is important to accurately identify your client's level of motivation by finding the current stage of change in which they exist during an assessment for each diagnosed or treatable problem.

However, assessing his or her stage of change does not stop with the assessment. It is an ongoing part of the treatment process. Again, clients do not cycle smoothly through the stages, and relapse is a regular and expected occurrence in therapy, whether substance use or mental health. Also, remember that clients should be approached differently based on their motivation stage. For example, a client in the rebellious precontemplation stage cannot be approached harshly and directly. A more indirect approach that relies on slowly and gently pointing out discrepancies in his or her story is better.

### Last Principle: When All Else Fails, Never Do Anything That Violates the First Principle!

This principle speaks for itself. If it will make your relationship oppositional, or if you are frustrated with your client's lack of progress, remember: Just. Don't. Do. It. In the end, if all else fails, practitioners can be nice, friendly, welcoming, and respectful. This attitude may help save a life someday because they remember how nice you were when it comes time to seek help seriously.

## SUMMARY

In this chapter, we introduced you to the Advance Multiple Systems (AMS) practice perspective. This approach, although not a specific practice method, provides a foundation for conceptualizing and thinking about clients from a multiple systems perspective, particularly as it relates to understanding, engaging, assessing, and treatment planning for the cases included in this text.

We also exposed you to the Guiding Practice Principles of AMS. These principles, like a professional code of ethics, offer a process for clinical decision making throughout the treatment process. We place a high value on the quality of relationships and solid personal choices always made in the client's best interest. We discussed the positive value of practitioners working to become the professional who promotes trusting and respectful therapeutic relationships as the foundation for successful practice. We believe the best practitioners are personally insightful, attending to their personal biases, practice privilege, and relationships in a way that enhances their client's chance to succeed.

In the end, the following paragraph provides an excellent summary of the values and practices discussed in this chapter:

## CORE BELIEFS

Clients do not change because of models, methods, or interventions alone. They change because they are helped into a trusting and respectful therapeutic relationship based on enhancing their dignity as human beings, have hope they can change for the better, and the motivation to endure the process of change. All of this is accomplished in the context of helpful and supportive systems of support to build personal resilience.

# REFERENCES

Appleby, G. A. (2001). Dynamics of oppression and discrimination. In G. A. Appleby, E. Colon, & J. Hamilton (Eds.), *Diversity, oppression, and social functioning: Person-in-environment assessment and intervention*. Allyn & Bacon.

Connors, G. J., Donovan, D. M., & DiClemente, C. C. (2001). *Selecting and planning interventions: Substance abuse treatment and the stages of change*. Guilford Press.

Denning, P. (2000). *Practicing harm reduction psychotherapy: An alternative approach to addictions*. Guilford Press.

DiClemente, C. C. (1991). Motivational interviewing and the stages of change. In W. R. Miller & S. Rollnick (Eds.), *Motivational interviewing: Preparing people to change addictive behavior* (pp. 191–202). Guilford Press.

DiClemente, C. C., & Hughes, S. O. (1990). Stages of change profiles in outpatient alcoholism treatment. *Journal of Substance Abuse, 2*, 217–235.

DiClemente, C. C., & Prochaska, J. O. (1985). Processes and stages of change: Coping and competence in smoking behavior change. In S. Shiffman & T. A. Wills (Eds.), *Coping and substance abuse*. Academic Press.

Fong, R. (2001). Culturally competent social work practice: Past and present. In R. Fong & S. Furuto (Eds.), *Culturally competent practice: Skills, interventions, and evaluations*. Allyn & Bacon.

Freire, P. (1993). *Pedagogy of the oppressed*. Continuum.

Germain, C. B., & Gitterman, A. (1996). *The life model of social work practice* (2nd ed.). Columbia University Press.

Johnson, J. L. (2004). *Fundamentals of substance abuse practice*. Brooks/Cole.

Johnson, J. L. (2000). *Crossing borders—confronting history: Intercultural adjustment in a post-Cold War world*. University Press of America.

Johnson, J. L., & Grant, G. (2007). *Casebook: Sexual abuse*. Allyn & Bacon.

Johnson, J. L. & Grant, G. (2006). *Casebook: Mental health*. Allyn & Bacon.

Johnson, J. L., & Grant, G. (2005). *Casebook: Substance abuse*. Allyn & Bacon.

Kozol, J. (1991). *Savage inequalities: Children in America's schools*. Crown.

Leigh, J. W. (1998). *Communicating for cultural competence*. Allyn & Bacon.

Longres, J. F. (2000). *Human behavior in the social environment* (3rd ed.). F. E. Peacock.

Lum, D. (1999). *Culturally competent practice*. Brooks/Cole.

McLaren, P. (1995). *Critical pedagogy and predatory culture: Oppositional politics in a postmodern era*. Routledge.

Miller, W. R., & Rollnick, S. (2002). *Motivational interviewing: Preparing people to change addictive behavior* (2nd ed.). Guilford Press.

Miller, W. R., & Rollnick, S. (1991). *Motivational interviewing: Preparing people to change addictive behavior*. Guilford Press.

Mills, C. W. (1959). *The sociological imagination*. Oxford University Press.

Pinderhughes, E. (1989). *Understanding race, ethnicity, and power.* Free Press.

Polgar, A. T. (2017). Hope theory as social work treatment. In F. J. Turner (Ed.), *Social work treatment: Interlocking theoretical approaches* (6th ed., pp. 222–275). Oxford University Press.

Prochaska, J. O., & DiClemente, C. C. (1986). Toward a comprehensive model of change. In W. R. Miller & N. Heather (Eds.), *Treating addictive behaviors: Processes of change* (pp. 3–27). Plenum Press.

Prochaska, J. O., & DiClemente, C. C. (1984). *The transtheoretical approach: Crossing traditional boundaries of therapy.* Dow Jones/Irwin.

Prochaska, J. O., & DiClemente, C. C. (1982). Transtheoretical therapy: Toward a more integrative model of change. *Psychotherapy: Theory, Research, and Practice, 19,* 276–288.

Snyder, C. R. (2002). Hope theory: Rainbows in the mind. *Psychological Inquiry, 13*(4), 249–275.

Timberlake, E. M., Farber, M. Z., & Sabatino, C. A. (2002). *The general method of social work practice: McMahon's generalist perspective* (4th ed.). Allyn & Bacon.

What is privilege? (2019). Online://www.njcc.org/what-privilege.

# CHAPTER 2

# Child Protective Services

*George Grant, Jr.*

## INTRODUCTION

The gateway to the foster care system is child protective services (CPS). By federal law, every state has a CPS system in place for the well-being of children. The role of CPS is based on the Federal Child Abuse Prevention and Treatment Act (CAPTA), established in 1974. The act identifies areas of child abuse and neglect, state mandates, and mandated reporters. Mandated reporters are individuals who by law must report when they have evidence or suspect that a child is being abused or neglected. While we would like everyone to report child abuse and neglect, not everyone is treated as a mandated reporter.

Communities have two main ways to report child abuse and neglect; one is having a CPS division within the child welfare system at the county and state levels. The other is to report child abuse and neglect through law enforcement. This report is made to local, county, state, or federal law enforcement institutions.

A CPS worker will have several investigations in different stages of completion open at the same time. In this case study, we will follow Regina Copeland, a CPS worker employed by the County Department of Social Services. She has three cases you will follow to completion. Those cases are Mother's Mental Health Needs (the Tate Family), Infant in Distress (Ryan Wheeler Jr.), and A Call from School (Curtis and William Hall). As you follow Regina, you have the opportunity to conduct your investigation, assess the possible risk to the children involved, and determine if at the end of the investigation you would close the case or petition the court to open the case.

## THE INTAKE

The intake begins when the CPS intake worker receives a complaint about child abuse or neglect by phone, fax, or a person walking in to file a complaint. Most referrals come from mandated reporters. However, non-mandated reporters, unsure whom to call, along with calling CPS will call their local law enforcement, fire department, hospital, religious leader, or a crisis line for help.

One example is an intake CPS worker who receives a phone call about possible child abuse. The person may or may not identify themselves, but generally, they will if they are a mandated reporter. The caller shares information about what they believe is abuse or neglect happening to a child. The intake worker's job is to conduct a risk assessment to determine if there should be an investigation, and the case is assigned to a CPS worker.

When people call CPS, the CPS intake worker has to take the information and assess if there is a case worthy of investigation. The vast majority of cases are not opened or investigated because they do not score high enough on the risk assessment protocol. Some of the reasons cases are not opened include people calling the wrong number, calling about non-child neglect issues, calling for services, or supports where a different organization or agency is needed to provide those services. CPS also gets its share of drunk phone calls, prank calls, and people mad at each other trying to get the other person in trouble and having their children removed from the home.

Once the intake worker gathers as much information as possible, they determine if the case should be opened. There are different risk assessment tools that agencies use to determine risk levels for opening a case. In addition to the assessment tools, some determinations are made solely by the intake worker. Others must talk with another worker before deciding to open a case, and in other situations, all cases go to the supervisor, who makes the final decision whether a case should be opened for further investigation. In the County Department of Social Services, all cases are reviewed by an internal committee to determine if there is an agreement regarding opening or not opening the case.

---

### QUESTIONS

1. Find a copy of the Child Abuse Prevention and Treatment Act.
2. Review how child abuse and neglect are defined and what situations would qualify as child abuse and neglect.
3. Review the individuals listed as mandated reporters.
4. Define a mandated reporter.
5. Determine if your professor qualifies as a mandated reporter according to the policy.
6. Based on the policy, as a student, are you a mandated reporter? Explain why you are or are not.
7. Review the professional literature on risk assessment tools.
8. Select one of the tools and review the literature on the factors used to determine if a case scores high enough for an investigation.

9. What are the attributes used in the tool you selected?

10. Further in the case, once the intake worker has completed her assessment, you will review the information based on the risk assessment tool you selected. You will see if you came to the same conclusion as the intake worker.

---

## MOTHER'S MENTAL HEALTH NEEDS: THE TATE FAMILY

### Mother's Mental Health

It was late morning when the phone rang, and the CPS intake worker responded. On the phone was Lois Tate, a grandmother who was concerned about her daughter and her two grandchildren. Lois Tate and her husband, Bishop Tate, had not heard from their daughter or grandchildren in three days.

Their daughter, Laura Tate, had been dealing with some mental health issues and was seeing a counselor. There were times when Laura did not get out of bed or get the children ready for school. Sometimes Laura would forget to buy groceries or let the children stay awake past their bedtimes. Family members found Laura a counselor because Laura said she would sometimes hear voices, or thought she heard voices. While it did not happen often, it often meant the children were not cared for as they should be, noted Lois.

Lois explained that she and her husband had been helping out their daughter and grandchildren. There was a seven-year-old son, Samuel, and a five-year-old daughter, Mary. The grandparents would often take the children to their home to give their daughter a break. Lois also said they enjoyed having the grandchildren around.

Lois added that Laura had abused alcohol and drugs but said she had recently quit. However, in the last several months Laura began showing erratic behaviors again. There were times Laura would answer the phone, but not say anything. Lois would go to her house, and while hearing her movement inside, Laura would not come to the door.

Laura seemed to be making progress in counseling. Lois and her husband were hopeful she would get her life together and take good care of her children. That was, until three days ago. Without explanation, Lois could not reach Laura.

The intake worker asked Lois if Laura had any other family or friends to stay with. Lois claimed that the last time she talked to her daughter, Laura was taking her children to visit a friend over the weekend. She planned to be back in time for the children to go to school on Monday. This was the only friend Lois knew. They had no other family living in the state.

The intake worker asked if Laura had ever physically hurt the children, but Lois said no. "Laura may not always take care of the children, but she had not harmed them."

In hindsight, Lois believed her daughter was talking erratically. Over the years Lois had become used to the erratic, disjointed conversations and placed no more emphasis on them than previous ones. Lois had talked to both children, and they seemed fine, so she did not worry about the friend visit.

When Monday came, Lois called her daughter, and Laura said she was not feeling well. Laura said they had a good time, and she would talk to her later. Monday, Tuesday, and Wednesday came and went, and they heard nothing from Laura, and after unanswered phone calls, going to the house with no answer, and not having a key to enter the home, they called the counselor. The counselor suggested they call CPS.

The intake worker took down additional information, including any identifying information, ages, birth dates, distinguishing characteristics, and any other information the grandparent thought would be helpful. Once the intake worker had the address and phone number for Laura, she also took down contact information for the grandparents.

The intake worker asked about the biological father, and Lois said that his name was John Boyd. According to Lois, Boyd was in prison in another state. Neither Laura nor the children had any contact with John.

## QUESTIONS

1.  As an intake worker, based on the information that you received, were there questions that you thought the intake worker did not ask?
2.  Based on the Child Abuse Prevention and Treatment Act, were the grandparents mandated reporters? Explain why they were or were not.
3.  Based on the information you have, use the risk assessment tool you selected to determine if the case reached a score to identify this as a high-risk case.

## Regina Copeland

The case was assigned to CPS worker Regina Copeland. Regina had been a CPS worker for 13 years. While for some, 13 years was a long time to be a CPS worker, Regina did not see it that way. She believed she was making a difference in protecting children and helping families. This was the reason she got into social work, and once she learned about CPS, she knew it was what she wanted to do. Regina has turned down multiple opportunities to move into management roles to stay connected to day-to-day contact with clients.

Regina received the Tate case from the intake worker. After reviewing the information in the file, she decided to go to Laura Tate's apartment. Every case is different, and based on the recommendation of the intake worker, supervisor, or the worker's own instinct, they would decide to conduct the investigation alone, with another CPS worker, or with someone from law enforcement.

Based on the information, Regina decided she would investigate this case by herself. There was no evidence of violence or prior police involvement. Moreover, the information from the grandparents showed that until recently, they had regular contact with their daughter and grandchildren.

When Regina arrived, she saw a series of single-story apartments connected in groups of four. The apartment layout was the same on both sides of the street. The Tate apartment was the second in from the left. Each apartment has a small front yard and a tiny porch. On the front of the Tate apartment, all of the curtains were closed, preventing any sunlight from shining in. Standing on the porch, she gave the doorbell three quick taps. After no response, she knocked on the door. Still no response. Standing on the porch, you could knock on the front windows, so she moved to her left and tapped on the window. At that point, she thought she heard movement. She wondered if the tapping on the window startled the person inside because they were only expecting the doorbell or a knock on the door. She tapped gently on the window this time and said hello.

She did not hear any more sounds coming from inside the house, but then the curtain moved. She took a step back so whoever was in the window could get a better look at her. Regina said hello again. The curtain opened, and a young face was looking out the window at her. She waved at the boy, and shyly he waved back. In a calm, friendly voice, she asked if his mother was at home. He nodded his head up and down. Regina asked if his mother was okay, and the boy shook his head.

Regina thought about calling the police to force the door open for a welfare check, but she thought she would try the young boy one last time. Based on the case information, she assumed the boy looking out the window was Samuel.

"Samuel, I am here to help you, your sister Mary, and your mother to make sure that everyone is okay. Your grandmother asked me to come over. Is it okay for you to open the door?"

She smiled at him and nodded her head as if she agreed with her own words. Sammy looked at her for what seemed like a long time, and then the curtains shut again. She knew she needed to get in the house, and if no one opened the door, she would have to call the police for assistance.

She reached in her pocket for her cell phone to call for assistance when she heard a click. As she stood there the door slowly opened and there stood Samuel.

There was no storm door so she could have walked in the front door. She kneeled to make eye contact with him.

"Hello," she said, and smiled at him. He smiled back. "Are you Samuel?" she asked. He nodded. "My name is Regina, and I'm here to help. Does your mother need any help?"

Samuel did not say anything but nodded. Regina asked if she could come in to check on his mother and sister. His first word was, "Yes," and opened the door further for Regina to come in.

Regina walked into a house that was mostly dark except for the light now coming through the front door. She asked Samuel if it was okay if she opened the curtains, and he nodded. Sunlight poured into the room as the curtains opened. Turning back to Samuel she asked if that was his name. He said yes. She asked where his mother and sister were, and Samuel pointed to the back of the house. Regina called out for Laura Tate, identified herself by name, and that she was with Child Protective Services there to help. She heard movement coming from the back room.

Regina walked a short distance down the hall past a bedroom and bathroom to the door in the back of the house. She first saw the bed with the little girl lying on it. She assumed it was Mary, but she would find out in a moment. She waved at the little girl, and the little girl waved back. She didn't see the mother until she stepped fully into the room. Further to her right was an adult woman who was sitting on the floor, leaning against the wall. It appeared she was talking to herself, or, in a different situation, you might say she was quietly singing.

Regina took a couple of steps toward the lady and said, "Hello, my name is Regina. I'm from Child Protective Services, and your family is concerned about you and wanted me to check on you. Are you Laura Tate?" Regina asked.

The lady continued to talk to herself and not look up or acknowledge Regina. At that point, she reached into her pocket, pulled out her phone, and called for an ambulance.

Regina continued to ask Laura questions. She touched Laura's shoulder looking for a response, but Laura did not look up.

"Did you hit your head on the wall?" Regina asked. There was no response. "Would you like to lie down? I can help you lie on the floor."

Laura continued to talk in a low voice. Regina could not make out a single word. Laura was sitting at an awkward angle, so Regina slowly moved her leg from under her and turned her a little, so more of her back was against the wall. From that position, Regina could see more of her face and body. Laura did not appear to be in any pain. She moved into the new position without any hesitation or refusal. Regina continued talking to her, but there was still no acknowledgment that she was in the room.

She then went to check on the children. She stopped at the bed where Mary lay.

"Can you tell me your name?"

"Mary," said the little girl.

"I'm Regina. Your grandparents asked me to come over to help your family. Are you okay, Mary?"

She nodded.

"Have you had anything to eat today?"

Mary shook her head. "I'm hungry."

"How about you, Samuel? You hungry, too?"

"Yes, ma'am. We haven't had food in a while."

Samuel was the older of the two children, so Regina decided to get information from him.

"Samuel, are there any foods either you or Mary can't eat?"

"Nope ... we eat anything ..."

"Okay, good! I"ll get you something to eat in just a few minutes."

While Regina wanted to give the children something to eat, she decided to wait for the medical services to arrive so the children could be checked before they ate anything. She wanted medical onsite in case the children did have food allergies and reacted badly to the food.

Regina asked Samuel and Mary to go with her into the front room. There was a couch, chairs, and several toys on the floor. She took a seat on the couch and asked the children to pick out toys to play with. While the children played in the living room, she moved back and forth between the children in the living room and Laura in the back bedroom to make sure all was well until the ambulance arrived.

She told the children her mother would get help, their grandparents would meet them at the hospital, and she would stay with them to make sure that everyone was okay.

Regina called the office to provide an update on the case. CPS workers often investigate new cases by themselves. However, even when they have a partner, they still must check in with their office as part of the safety protocol. Regina gave the office worker an update and asked him to call Laura's parents and arrange for them to meet at the local hospital.

Regina could hear the ambulance coming. She returned to the bedroom to try speaking to Laura again. Although Laura had not communicated with her, Regina explained again who she was and informed her that an ambulance had arrived to check on her and the children. She also informed Laura that she and her children would be transported to the hospital, where they would be met by her parents.

Suddenly, Laura stopped talking to herself, looked up at Regina, and said, "Thank you." She immediately looked back away and began talking to herself again.

Regina went back into the front room to check on the children and make sure they were safe.

The ambulance arrived, and paramedics immediately went to the back room to check on Laura while Regina stayed with the children. They placed Laura on a stretcher and moved her to the ambulance for transport. One of the paramedics talked to both children and did a quick checkup to make sure that there were no injuries on either child. Finding none, the children were also placed in the ambulance and taken to the hospital.

Regina called the agency again and asked for a background check on the grandparents to make sure that there were no CPS complaints or criminal investigations to assess if the children would be safe in their care.

### QUESTIONS

1. Since there was an agreement that Lois and Bishop Tate were the grandparents, why would the CPS workers have any hesitation about placing the children with them?
2. Assess the interaction between Laura and Regina. Discuss as the CPS worker how you would have handled the interaction differently.
3. Are there questions that you would have asked the children that Regina did not ask?
4. As you continue working the case, see if you can determine why Samuel opened the door for Regina, but neither Samuel nor Mary opened the door for their grandparents?

Regina drove to the hospital to wait for updates on Laura and the children. Once at the hospital, she went to the hospital social work office to check in and give them an update on the family. The hospital social worker would stay in contact with the doctors and nurses and give Regina updates on how the family was doing. Regina also informed them that the grandparents were coming to the hospital so they could be brought to the social work office to wait for information.

## The Grandparents

Lois and Bishop arrived at the hospital about 30 minutes later and were escorted to the social work office. Regina took them into an office and talked with them about the case, what she found out, and about the two children. Before the grandparents got to the hospital, Regina got a follow-up phone call that there were no CPS investigations or criminal record on the grandparents.

Regina gathered a social history on Laura Tate and the family from the grandparents. The hospital social worker came in and asked the grandparents if there were any medical issues, food allergies, or other information the doctor needed to know about Samuel and Mary. With the information provided and once the medical exam was complete, the children could eat something, and their grandparents could sit with them.

Regina asked the grandparents if they would be willing to take Samuel and Mary into their home because she would be filing a petition with the court for temporary foster care and the removal of Samuel and Mary. The grandparents readily agreed to take the children.

They asked if she knew what would happen to Laura.

Regina responded, "Laura will be assessed by professionals to determine if she was experiencing either a medical or mental issue causing her current behavior. Then doctors will recommend the kind of help she needs. I will not have any additional information until the doctor or social worker comes and presents that to them."

## The Court

Regina contacted her supervisor to inform him that she would be going to court to file a petition to have the children placed in relative care and assigned to a local foster care agency. The supervisor supported the recommendation, and Regina left the hospital and headed to court.

The agency completed the petition and faxed it to the court. When Regina got to court, she reviewed the information, signed the form, and gave it to the court clerk. In this county, a referee presides over the preliminary hearings. If the decision is made to open a case, the referee writes a court order for the children's placement in foster care and assigns the case to a judge for a formal hearing within 30 days.

Laura would be assigned a court-appointed attorney. The children would receive a separate attorney. Although the father is in prison, he would also be assigned an attorney. A county assistant prosecutor is assigned to represent the interests of the people of the county.

Regina met with the assistant prosecutor and the referee to discuss the case. The referee determined that there was sufficient evidence to demonstrate the safety and well-being of the children would be better served in foster care. Since the Tates (the grandparents) were able to provide for the children, the court order included the children's placement with them.

## Closing the Case

Regina went back to the hospital and met with the grandparents to explain that the children were placed in their care and that the case would be assigned to a foster care agency who would work with them, the children, and their daughter. Regina explained about the court hearing in 30 days, the court-appointed attorneys, and the foster care agency they would be working with.

The grandparents were relieved that their grandchildren would be placed with them, and they thanked Regina for all of her help. She told them a police officer would come and go with them to the daughter's house to get clothes, toys, and school supplies for the children. A foster care worker would contact them and start working with their daughter once the doctor had determined what her needs were and placement options.

Once back in the office, she completed all of the paperwork, provided an update to her supervisor, sent the information to the foster care agency, talked to the foster care worker, and closed the case on the Tate family.

### QUESTIONS

1. Before a CPS worker can take a case to court, they must show that the children are at risk for continued abuse or neglect if they remain in the home. Discuss how these risks factors were determined in this case.
2. Provide a preliminary assessment based on the information you have on this case.
3. Discuss why the mother, father, and children would have separate attorneys since they are one family.
4. Discuss why the grandparents were not appointed an attorney.
5. Based on the literature, what is the role of the assistant prosecutor in foster care cases?
6. Research the role of the judge in foster care cases.
7. Based on the professional literature, what is the role of the parent's attorney?
8. Based on the professional literature, what is the role of the children's attorney?
9. In most cases, when there is more than one child, they all get the same attorney. Review why each child would not get their own attorney.
10. At the end of a case, there are always unanswered questions. List questions you still have about the Tate case.
11. Were you able to assess why the children did not open the door for the grandparents?

## INFANT IN DISTRESS: RYAN WHEELER JR.

### A Case Assignment

Regina was in her office doing paperwork when the intake worker came in and gave her a new case. The case involved neighbors calling on a family in their neighborhood with an infant they believed the parents were not feeding correctly. They felt that the infant was underweight and in distress and that the parents were not capable of providing the kind of care the infant needed. They felt terrible about making the call, but the infant was their top priority. They knew the parents and tried to provide support, but the parents had a difficult time understanding what the infant needed and providing the kind of care the infant required.

The people making the referral, August Wells and Robert Ruiz, gave their names, address, and phone number, saying they would be happy to talk to the Child Protective Services (CPS) worker and provide any additional information the person needed. August and Robert gave the names of the couple they were calling on, Deborah Graham, 26, Ryan Wheeler, 25, and their nine-month-old son, Ryan Jr.

As part of the file, the intake worker looked to see if there had been any CPS referrals on Deborah Graham or Ryan Wheeler. After a thorough review, she found that there had been no complaints about the family, including none from medical professionals. Regina thought this could indicate the parents were keeping their medical appointments, but it was always possible that the parents were changing doctors, so there was no pattern for a medical professional to make a CPS referral.

August and Robert were not mandated reporters, just neighbors and friends who were concerned about an infant. While the intake worker greatly appreciated it, she also knew that it was rare for neighbors to call CPS on each other. It did happen, but the likelihood from her years of experience was rare that this kind of call would come in. Therefore, the intake worker also checked to see if there were any previous investigations on August and Robert. As she went through the records, she found that August Wells and Robert Ruiz have two children, ages nine and five, in foster care. During the CPS investigation, the parents said the nine-year-old was riding her bike when she fell and broke her arm. They took her to emergency, and the doctor felt the break was inconsistent with a child falling off a bike. After talking to the parents and getting inconsistent answers, they contacted CPS. The CPS worker came to the hospital to investigate the complaint, and after going over the medical information with the doctor and talking to the parents and children, he felt that there were sufficient grounds to petition the court to open a case and placement of the children in foster care.

There was also a note in the file of August and Robert complaining they were good parents and couldn't understand why their children were in foster care when they had neighbors like Deborah and Ryan who had an infant that they were not smart enough to take care of, and yet that child was still with them while their children were in foster care.

Unfortunately, CPS will get referrals from people who are mad at their neighbors or friends and as a way to punish them, will call CPS to have the children removed and placed in foster care. Based on the referral and what August and Robert had said, the intake worker and Regina wondered if this was one of those cases.

QUESTIONS

1.  Using your risk assessment tool, does Ryan Jr. score in the range to open a case and conduct an investigation?
2.  Provide detail on why you would or would not open a case on Ryan Jr.

Regina took all of the information and set out to meet Deborah and Ryan. Based on the assessment, an investigation was needed to ensure Ryan Jr. was safe. While she had concerns about the source of the referral, the infant still could be in distress and need assistance. The challenge for CPS is deciding which cases to go out on. All their data shows that with the majority of CPS calls, there is no abuse or neglect. They also know there are higher incidents of substantiated abuse and neglect in specific zip codes, socioeconomic classes, education, and ethnic groups. They also know that people are less likely to call CPS on middle- and upper-class families, public figures, and those in positions of power.

QUESTIONS

1.  Looking at your state, what socioeconomic groups and what ethnic groups get the highest number of calls to CPS on them?
2.  Review the literature on why the number of calls on those groups are higher than other groups.

## Ryan and Deborah

Regina got to the duplex and noticed that August and Robert's house was across the street and two houses down. She wondered if they were looking at her. The neighborhood was made up of blocks of low-income duplexes. This community has one of the highest call rates to CPS. There is only one zip code in the county with a higher number of children removed from their biological parents and placed in foster care. This zip code also has one of the highest rates of parental rights terminations and the children placed for adoption. Regina hated that she knew those statistics because it tipped the risk assessment scale to include that information when deciding whether to investigate individual cases. Are those areas more likely to abuse or neglect their children, or are we spending more time trying to find abuse and neglect?

She knocked on the door, waiting in anticipation on who was on the other side. Not everyone was happy to see CPS at their home. There was no definite reason for us to show up, people would say. Ryan came to the door.

Holding up her ID, Regina said, "Hello, I am Regina Copeland. I am with Child Protective Services, and I am looking for Mr. Wheeler and Ms. Graham."

She always used peoples last names until they told her she could use their first name. She believed in showing everyone respect from the way you talk to people to how you dress. Regina did not have different standards based on socioeconomic status.

"I am Ryan," he said.

"Hello, Ryan. Sometimes we get a call that a family or children may need our help. When we get a call, we send someone out to help. That is why I'm here. We got a call that you may need help with Ryan Jr. Is that his name?"

Ryan listened intently as Regina talked. When she finished, he stood there as if waiting for her to say more. Regina noticed the silence and asked, "Is it okay if I come in?'

Ryan gave an expression like he now understood, and said, "Yes. Please come in."

He let her in and called for Deborah. Regina introduced herself to Deborah and explained again why she was there.

Regina found it interesting how every family responded to her differently. Some were very open and welcoming, while others were hostile and almost abusive in how they treated her. There were a few times she had to make up a story to get out of the house because she thought they were going to hurt her. There were also times she needed a police officer to go with her for protection and to keep things calm. No two families were the same, and you never knew what to expect when the door opened.

Ryan and Deborah were warm and inviting and asked her to take a seat.

"Would you like something to drink?" asked Deborah. Regina politely declined, but she did take a seat in the chair. They sat on the couch.

The apartment was sparse with little furniture and a couple of infant toys. While talking to the parents, they were very calm and didn't appear nervous about her being there. Regina noticed a slowness in the way they talked and answered questions. It didn't come across like they were hesitating to come up with the right answer, it was more that their cognitive abilities or level of interaction were just at a slower pace than what people would perceive as usual. She did not like that the word usual popped in her head, and she would find another way of expressing that when she wrote her report.

Regina asked, "How is Ryan Jr. doing?"

"He is wonderful," Deborah said. "My little angel." Deborah talked about how healthy and happy he is, and how much they enjoy having him in their lives.

"Have you been able to take him to his doctor's appointments?"

Ryan said, "We have made every one. There was one we thought we were going to miss because the bus was running late. But once we got to the office, we still got to see the doctor."

"I'm sorry to ask this, but is it okay if I see Ryan Jr.?"

Deborah and Ryan appeared not to have a problem with the request. Deborah led Regina to the bedroom. There was a crib against the wall with Ryan Jr. lying there quietly. His eyes followed Deborah as she walked toward him.

"He is beautiful. Can I hold him?"

They said yes, and Regina reached into the crib to pick him up. She talked to Ryan Jr. in a low soft voice while holding him. She was trained in how to interact with infants and children to check for signs of abuse or neglect without looking like you were investigating or violating the child's privacy.

She saw no bruises or marks on Ryan Jr. Moreover, while she did not have a scale, she did have a basic understanding of a nine-month-old's weight, and he did not appear to be malnourished, underweight, or neglected. She asked them if they were okay with her contacting their doctor, and they found a piece of paper to write down the doctor's name, address, and phone number. There was no hesitation in them sharing this information.

## QUESTIONS

1. Regina talked about respecting the privacy of children when examining them. While conducting a visual investigation, does the literature describe ways to do a physical exam while maintaining the dignity of the child?

2. Write a two-page assessment of the Wheeler-Graham family based on the information you have.

With the spartan conditions, she wanted to make sure that there was food, running water, and heat in the home. It was just turning spring, so there was a need to have the heat on, and she could tell that the home was warm. In her case, she thought it was a little too warm, but that was her problem. She asked about the food for Ryan Jr., and they took her into the kitchen and showed that there was more than enough food for at least the next month. He also turned on the sink, and she saw that there was running water.

"Is there anything I can help you with?"

They looked at each other before Ryan answered. "I can't think of anything. We have a caseworker who is very helpful."

"She is a nice lady," Deborah added, "and she loves Ryan Jr. She cannot wait to see him."

Regina got the name of the caseworker and would follow up with her.

**QUESTIONS**

1. Based on information provided by Regina on this case, explain if you would open or not open a case on Ryan Jr.
2. Discuss what information you would like to have that was not provided in this case on Deborah, Ryan, and Ryan Jr.

Regina thanked Deborah and Ryan for letting her into their home and for the opportunity to meet Ryan Jr. She told them what a great baby he was, how calm and quiet he was, and she appreciated all that they were doing to provide for him. She also explained once again that when someone calls CPS, they have to come out and check on the child.

She thanked them for their understanding, and she gave each of them one of her business cards, telling them if she could be of any help, or help connecting them to an organization or service that they needed, all they had to do was call her. There is also a community resource book which lists all the different agencies in the county and the services that they provide. Regina always carries a number of them to give out to families.

She thanked them again, said goodbye to Ryan Jr., and left.

**QUESTION**

1. The people who made the complaint live two houses away. Should Regina stop at their house to see if there is any additional information they wanted to share? Discuss your decision and the reasoning behind that decision.

## The Family Across the Street

Regina walked to her car, turned back and waved at the family, and waited for them to close the door. She got in her car and sat there for a few minutes, hoping the family didn't come back to the door or come out. When she thought enough time had passed, she got out of her car and walked over to August and Robert's house.

Their duplex looked the same as Deborah and Ryan's from the outside. She rang the doorbell, and a man came to the door. She introduced herself, showed her CPS ID, and asked for Mr. Ruiz and Ms. Wells. Robert seemed excited to see her and quickly ushered her into the house. He called for August, and she came around the corner. He quickly said this is the CPS worker. August, like Robert, seemed excited and asked her to sit down.

As Regina looked around the home, it appeared dirty and had a strong unpleasant smell to it. There was a cloth couch and plastic chairs in the living room. Against one wall was a stand with a large television and a cable box.

August was the first to talk. "We saw you across the street. Did you take the baby?" she asked in an excited tone. "We know they are terrible parents, and we just could not sit around and let that baby suffer like that. It hurt us to call you, but we knew it was the right thing to do."

Robert added, "I feel sorry for the baby being raised by parents like that. If we could take him into our home, we would care for him and protect him."

Regina asked them if it was okay if she took notes while they talked, and they readily agreed.

"Can you tell me what you have witnessed that brought this concern to your attention and the need to call CPS?"

They each talked about the family's inability to care for the baby. Robert said, "There was not enough food in the home, the child seemed malnourished, and we didn't know what parenting skills they had." August added that they had gone to the house on numerous occasions, offering any help, but the family didn't want any.

Robert said, "I thought there was something wrong with the parents mentally and that maybe they were incapable of understanding how to care for a child."

Regina asked several additional questions about how many times they'd been over there, what they had witnessed, the kind of care they saw Deborah and Ryan provide for Ryan Jr., and what did they think should happen to Ryan Jr.?

They did not know how many times they'd been over to the house but said "a lot." August once again talked about how much she worries about Ryan Jr. and that she was glad that I was investigating the family. "That child needs a safe home," she said.

Regina thanked them for their concern and for calling CPS. She let them know that she could not share any information with them about the family, but she would make sure Ryan Jr. got the best care possible. She thanked them again and got up to leave.

At the door, Robert said, "If there is anything we can do to help, just let us know." Regina went back to her car and drove away.

## QUESTIONS

1. What Regina saw in the home and what August and Robert described as what was happening in the home were different. List some reasons why you think there would be differences in describing the same family.

2. Based on the Child Protection Act, what information can Regina legally share with August and Robert about the Ryan Jr. case?

3. During your meeting with August and Robert, develop a list of questions that you would ask them that were not included in Regina's questions.

---

## A CALL FROM SCHOOL: CURTIS AND WILLIAM HALL

### A Call from School

The CPS intake worker got a call from an elementary school social worker regarding two brothers who came to school each with a bruise on their face. Because the call came from a mandated reporter and there were visual marks on the children, he opened the case and called the on-call CPS worker. While he completed the risk assessment tool, there was an unwritten policy that most calls from mandated reporters are opened and a CPS worker assigned to investigate the case. While it was rare to have a mandated reporter make up information, there was also the politics of not opening a case and the mandated reporter publicly saying how CPS does not care about children or is trying to say money, or they don't place a priority on poor children. They had heard this in the past when the risk assessment tool did not score high enough to open a case. Therefore, to avoid most of those complaints, they decided to open a case when it came from a mandated reporter. In this case, it scored high on the risk assessment tool so that the case would have been opened anyway.

Regina Copeland was in her car when she got the call from the CPS intake worker about possible abuse of two brothers called in by the school social worker. The intake worker went over the case on the phone and emailed the intake information to Regina so she could read it before going into the school.

Arriving at the school, Regina read her email to gain a better understanding of the case and to get the names of the people she would be talking to. Regina entered the school and walked to the main office. She identified herself, showing her ID, and asked for Mr. Kevin Reid. Regina sat on the bench and waited. They had worked on a number of cases, and Regina trusted Kevin's judgment.

Kevin Reid came out of the office, greeted Regina, and they went to the small conference room inside the main office area.

"It's been a while since they sent you to the school. I was starting to think you don't want to work with us anymore," said Kevin.

"There has been a big upturn in calls and removals. We don't know why, but something is going on. I have been all over the county, and my caseload continues to rise," said Regina.

They moved to the reason for the call. "I called on brothers Curtis Hall, age 12, and William Hall, age 11. William's teacher greets his students at the front entrance every morning. When William came in, the teacher saw the bruise on his face. When he asked William what happened, he would not answer, so he brought him to my office," said Kevin. "I already had been meeting with William and Curtis because they were having some challenges in school."

Both boys, Kevin said, have challenges in school from difficulty studying, staying focused, doing their homework, getting into fights, and not listening to their teachers.

"They can do some of the work, but it was clear that they were learning very little. After testing, both boys were placed in special education classrooms. This resulted in their behaviors getting lost because other children in the class exhibited behaviors far more extreme than theirs."

"Did the testing result in any medication for the boys?" asked Regina.

"The boys were diagnosed ADHD and placed on medication. Because of the school's concern that the parents would not follow through with giving the children their medication, the children receive their medication at school. The boys receive their medication every day they are in school, but sporadically on the weekend when the parents are responsible for administering medication, and no consistent pattern in the summertime when the children are out of school. With the lack of structure at home and during the summer when school was out, the boys have a difficult time adjusting to two different environments with different types of rules and expectations."

"Are the boys seeing a counselor?"

"Both boys have been meeting with me individually, and while Curtis does not trust anyone and only tells me a little about what is happening in the home, William is more comfortable with me and will share little details."

Regina asked, "Can you tell me about the conversations with the boys about the bruises?"

"After talking with William, I had Curtis brought to my office. He also had a bruise on his face. Curtis was less talkative than William and would not tell me what had happened. Once I told Curtis I knew what had happened; I could see the anger rise, not at me, but his brother," said Kevin.

"I told William to shut up. He has messed up everything," Curtis said to me.

"I tried to get additional information from him, but he sat quietly and would not say anything."

"I think it is time for me to meet Curtis and William. I think you should be in the room when I talk with them," said Regina.

Once Regina gathered the information from Kevin, she met with the boys separately with Kevin in the room. Curtis refused to say anything, got upset, and knocked his chair over in anger. In his discussions, William first sat quietly and over time repeated the story that he told Kevin Reid.

Their parents had been fighting, and in their anger, they struck the boys. It had happened before, but the parents would keep the children out of school to hide the bruises. This morning the parents overslept and Curtis got them ready for school. That was why this was the first time anyone saw bruises on them.

Once finished interviewing the boys, Regina went into another room to talk with Kevin. He asked a teacher's aide to stay with the boys until he got back.

"I still need to talk to their teachers. Why do you think Curtis's teacher did not tell you about the bruise?" Regina asked. Kevin wondered that same thing, but for now, his focus had been on the boys.

Regina told Kevin, "I believe there is enough information to petition the court while we decide if the boys will stay with their parents, if there are any relatives they can stay with, or for the removal of the boys to foster care."

Kevin nodded in agreement. "Curtis is so angry, and I don't know how he will do in foster care. My fear is he will run away from the foster home," said Kevin.

"My other concern is how mad Curtis is and will he need to take that anger out on someone. People tend to hurt the ones closest to them, and that would be William. Because William is the current cause of Curtis's problems, if I place them together, will Curtis hurt William?" said Regina.

She met with the teachers for any additional information and asked Kevin to stay with the boys while she went to the parents' house. Kevin would continue talking to the boys, with a focus on getting Curtis to reduce his anger toward William.

---

### QUESTIONS

1. Is a teacher a mandated reporter?
2. One teacher told the school social worker about the bruise. According to the child protection law, did the teacher fulfill their obligation, or should the teacher have called CPS?
3. Discuss why you think Curtis's teacher did not call CPS.
4. What is ADHD?
5. Identify several treatment options for a child with ADHD.

---

### The Hall Home

At the time of Regina's visit, the parents had been drinking and were in a heated fight. Standing on the front porch, she could hear the yelling coming from inside. She rang the doorbell and knocked on the door to get their attention. When the door opened, a man stood in front of her. Regina introduced herself and showed him her ID.

"Good morning. I am looking for Mr. and Mrs. Hall."
"I am David Hall," he said in a loud voice.
"Is it okay if I come in?" asked Regina.

David looked her up and down before agreeing to let her in. They stood in the hallway. He was not moving any further at the moment. Jane came out to the hallway, and Regina introduced herself to Jane, showing her ID.

It was clear that both parents had been drinking. She could smell the alcohol, and they both had trouble standing without leaning against the wall. She also heard them fighting about something and wondered how long they could stay in control of their behavior before they got mad at her or each other.

"Are you here about our children?" Jane asked.

Regina started to explain why she was there and the concern over the bruise on the faces of both children. Instead of asking them if they had hit the boys, she told them, "The school was concerned about the bruises and wanted to make sure you knew about them."

David and Jane looked at each other. Regina did not say anything else. She wanted to use the silence to see what they would say next. David spoke first.

"Did the school call the police?"

"No," she said. "They called Child Protective Services, and that is why I am here, to let you know about your children and to see if there is anything I can do to help."

David and Jane kept looking at each other. Regina could tell they were confused and were not sure what to say. She continued the silence until Jane broke it.

"Where are the boys?" Jane asked.

Regina told them, "The boys are at school. I have been to the school to make sure they were okay. Other than the bruises, the boys look fine."

"Do you know how the boys got the bruise on their faces?"

There was silence again. "Did they say we did it? Those boys fight with each other, and sometimes they get hurt. They are boys, they play rough," said David.

David continued talking about the boys roughhousing, and how they were good parents and would never hurt their children. Jane talked about how much they love their children, and how a mother would never hurt her children.

Regina could see the parents were starting to get agitated, talking louder and slowly moving toward her. She was glad she was in the hall standing by the door with nothing to block her exit if necessary. They still needed the wall to help them keep their balance, which would give her additional support if she needed to get out of the house.

She tried to calm them down, but their voices got louder as their anger turned to her. "You are not going to take our children. When you people show up, you always want to take their children. You are not taking ours. We are going to the school to get our children, and they better be there," said David. "It is time for you to leave our home."

Regina did not feel comfortable staying any longer. She handed them her card and left. In the car, she took a few deep breaths and called into the office to let them know she was fine. Regina filed a petition in court and requested the children be placed in temporary foster care while a full investigation was conducted.

At the end of the investigation, which included meeting with both parents, the boys, schoolteachers, the school social worker, and both boys having medical exams, there was evidence of abuse and neglect in the home, and there was evidence that the parents needed to make a number of changes in order to provide for their children. Curtis and William were placed in a temporary foster home.

### QUESTIONS

1. Based on the interaction between Regina and the parents, how would you have handled it differently?
2. Should Regina have told the parents that she would petition the court to have the boys placed in foster care? Explain your answer.
3. Do you agree with the decision to place the children in foster care? Discuss the reasoning behind your answer.
4. With the decision to place the children in foster care, would you place the boys in the same home or different homes? Discuss the reasoning for your answer.

## REFERENCES

Bride, B. E., Jones, J. L., & Macmaster, S. A. (2007). Correlates of secondary traumatic stress in child protective services workers. *Journal of Evidence-Based Social Work.* https://doi.org/10.1300/J394v04n03_05

Camasso, M. J., & Jagannathan, R. (2013). Decision making in child protective services: A risky business? *Risk Analysis.* http://doi.org/10.1111/j.1539-6924.2012.01931.x

Coohey, C., Johnson, K., Renner, L. M., & Easton, S. D. (2013). Actuarial risk assessment in child protective services: Construction methodology and performance criteria. *Children and Youth Services Review.* http://doi.org/10.1016/j.childyouth.2012.09.020

Courtney, M. E., & Hook, J. L. (2012). Evaluation of the impact of enhanced parental legal representation on the timing of permanency outcomes for

children in foster care. *Children and Youth Services Review.* http://doi.org/10.1016/j
.childyouth.2012.03.016

Cuccaro-Alamin, S., Foust, R., Vaithianathan, R., & Putnam-Hornstein, E. (2017).
Risk assessment and decision making in child protective services: Predictive risk
modeling in context. *Children and Youth Services Review.* http://doi.org/10.1016/j
.childyouth.2017.06.027

Edleson, J. L., Ellerton, A. L., Seagren, E. A., Kirchberg, S. L., Schmidt, S. O., &
Ambrose, A. T. (2007). Assessing child exposure to adult domestic violence. *Children and Youth Services Review.* https://doi.org/10.1016/j.childyouth.2006.12.009

Getway, C. W. I. (2013). *Long-term consequences of child abuse and neglect.* US Department of Health and Human Services, Children's Bureau.

Grasso, D., Boonsiri, J., Lipschitz, D., Guyer, A., Houshyar, S., Douglaspalumberi, H.,
... Kaufman, J. (2009). Posttraumatic stress disorder: The missed diagnosis. *Child Welfare.* http://doi.org/10.1111/j.1469-1795.2009.00289.x

Hughes, R. C., & Rycus, J. S. (2007). Issues in risk assessment in child protective
services. *Journal of Public Child Welfare.* http://doi.org/10.1300/J479v01n01_05

Jones, A. S., LaLiberte, T., & Piescher, K. N. (2015). Defining and strengthening child
well-being in child protection. *Children and Youth Services Review.* https://doi
.org/10.1016/j.childyouth.2015.05.001

King, C. B., & Scott, K. L. (2014). Why are suspected cases of child maltreatment
referred by educators so often unsubstantiated? *Child Abuse and Neglect.* https://
doi.org/10.1016/j.chiabu.2013.06.002

Lu, Y. E., Landsverk, J., Ellis-Macleod, E., Newton, R., Ganger, W., & Johnson, I. (2004).
Race, ethnicity, and case outcomes in child protective services. *Children and Youth
Services Review.* http://doi.org/10.1016/j.childyouth.2004.02.002

Palusci, V. J. (2011). Risk factors and services for child maltreatment among infants
and young children. *Children and Youth Services Review.* http://doi.org/10.1016/j
.childyouth.2011.04.025

Sattler, K. M. P., & Font, S. A. (2018). Resilience in young children involved with
child protective services. *Child Abuse and Neglect.* http://doi.org/10.1016/j
.chiabu.2017.05.004

Shlonsky, A., & Wagner, D. (2005). The next step: Integrating actuarial risk assessment and clinical judgment into an evidence-based practice framework in CPS
case management. *Children and Youth Services Review.* http://doi.org/10.1016/j
.childyouth.2004.11.007

Sykes, J. (2011). Negotiating stigma: Understanding mothers' responses to accusations of child neglect. *Children and Youth Services Review.* http://doi.org/10.1016/j
.childyouth.2010.06.015

Wilkins, D. (2015). Balancing risk and protective factors: How do social workers and
social work managers analyze referrals that may indicate children are at risk of significant harm. *British Journal of Social Work.* http://doi.org/10.1093/bjsw/bct114

Weisz, V., Wingrove, T., Beal, S. J., & Faith-Slaker, A. (2011). Children's participation in foster care hearings. *Child Abuse and Neglect.* http://doi.org/10.1016/j.chiabu.2010.12.007

Zeanah, C. H., & Humphreys, K. L. (2018). Child abuse and neglect. *Journal of the American Academy of Child and Adolescent Psychiatry.* https://doi.org/10.1016/j.jaac.2018.06.007

# CHAPTER 3

# The Adoption of Curtis and William

*George Grant, Jr.*

## INTRODUCTION

The simple sentence "The child has been placed in an adoptive home" requires multiple systems working together to make this outcome possible. This case study will present those moving parts and get them moving toward a permanency outcome. We will prepare two siblings for adoption, examining the systems that will influence how this placement happens. We will also follow a family navigating the child welfare system to become adoptive parents. Finally, we will explore how the two groups come together, along with the challenges they face as an adoptive family.

For an adoption to happen, there are five different—but overlapping—systems that must be united. The first system is all the people connected to the process that to some degree must come together. The people connected to the case include the biological parents, siblings, relatives, friends, judges, attorneys, foster care workers, therapist, adoption workers, adoptive parents, and their children, parents, relatives, friends, and community.

The next group is all the policy makers that influence child welfare. They include federal, state, and local legislators who pass laws that others must carry out in order for the adoption to happen. There are also advocacy groups, social groups, community organizations, and individuals who are concerned about how the child welfare system treats children, parents, extended relatives, adoptive families, and the role of race, religion, and socioeconomic status on the laws that are passed, how they are interpreted, and how people are treated. Their concern is social justice, but each group looks at social justice differently.

Next is all the paperwork requirements from intake reports, assessments, treatment plans, petitions, court reports, audits at multiple levels, child assessment reports, foster care home studies, adoption home studies, and adoption assessment reports.

There is the physical and emotional toll that the biological parents, adoptive family, foster care and adoption workers, therapist, children, and extended family all have to address and come to some resolution for the best interest of the child.

Along with the steps necessary to make the adoptive placement, there are numerous other factors to consider and address after the child is placed in the adoptive home. All of this happens so we can say a simple sentence: "The child has been placed in an adoptive home."

## WHAT IS ADOPTION?

The word *adoption* is usually associated with infants, domestic or international, going into a loving home, "a forever family," a family unable or deciding not to have biological children, wanting to increase their family, or having a calling to open their homes to infants in need. These are formal adoptions certified by a local court. There are adoption fees that must be signed off by the judge presiding over the adoption. In theory, this is to ensure that adoption agencies or brokers do not charge exorbitant fees to families who desperately want a child. There is also the debate over whether one is paying fees or buying a baby. Adoption fees can differ by judge, county, and state. There are also different fees for domestic adoptions and international adoptions. International adoption fees are higher than domestic adoptions. In both approaches, there is no one fee structure.

There are informal adoptions: a family member, fictive kin (those in close social relationships not based on blood or marriage), or friend takes a child into their home because the parents are unable to provide for the child, and the child becomes part of the extended family. Informal adoptions are not recognized by the legal system because there is no court involvement.

There are also children adopted through the foster care system where the children have experienced some form of abuse and neglect. The children range in age from infants through teenagers, and there can be large or small sibling groups. In these cases, through a Child Protective Services investigation, they find evidence of abuse and neglect by the parents and remove the children from the home. After providing services to the parents and the children, there can be a determination by the court that the parents have not made significant progress to have the children returned to their care. The court rules that in the foreseeable future, the parents will not make enough progress for the children to return home, and therefore a permanency plan must be developed for the children. One form of permanency by the court is having parental rights terminated, making the children eligible for adoption. Termination of parental rights means the biological parents are no longer the legal parents, as recognized by the court, and those children are placed for adoption.

It is easier to find adoptive homes for younger children and small sibling groups than for teenagers, large sibling groups, and children with physical and mental challenges that make it more difficult for the adoptive parents to handle. When an adoptive home is not possible, children may live in residential group homes, foster homes, or independent living arrangements until they can be adopted or until their emancipation between ages 18 and 21, depending on the state. There have been occasions when placements have been exhausted, and the teenager is returned to the parents whose parental rights were terminated.

Once the children are adopted, there can be challenges for the adoptive parents, children, and extended family. Some families don't have the skills to parent children who have experienced trauma. Some children, after living with years of rejection and broken placements, expect to be moved again and find it difficult to bond with the family. Other children will try and reject the family before the family can reject them. There are also children so connected to their biological family that they refuse to connect to another family out of a sense of loyalty. For some children, the dream will always be to return to their biological family.

## QUESTIONS

1. In foster care, what is termination of parental rights?
2. In your county, what is the process for adopting an infant that is not in the foster care system? Is there a difference between domestic and international adoptions in your county when it comes to paperwork requirements and court and attorney fees?
3. In this case, when a family adopts a child from the foster care system, all court and attorney fees are waived. Explain the fee policy in your state.

## ADOPTION RECRUITING

The adoption recruiter, Helene Gilmore, put her information packet together for her first home visit with Mr. and Mrs. Larry and Caroline Cannon to talk about being adoptive parents. As an adoption recruiter, Helene's job includes advertising, promoting, and recruiting people to be adoptive parents. She holds community information sessions, speaks at churches, social clubs, community events, businesses, and conferences—anyplace she can tell people about the wonders of adoption. She knows that adopting foster children is not for everyone. In her talks, she would say that most people can't imagine the kinds of harmful things that adults do to children. Helene gives examples of harm to children and watches the shocked looks on many of their faces. She had seen firsthand people say they can handle that information, only for an adoption disruption to occur and the child returned to foster care. She did not want to scare people, but she did want them to understand the realities of what children have experienced, and she did not need people who were shocked and sorry: she needed people who could overcome that shock and provide a safe, loving home, so the children could move on with their lives.

The other part of Helene's job is conducting adoptive home studies. This includes meeting the family several times, conducting an assessment, and deciding that they can be adoptive parents and what types of behaviors they can handle. Some families are not comfortable with children who have experienced sexual abuse because the child might act out some of those behaviors in the adoptive home. Other families have challenges with large sibling groups, and still others with children who still have contact with the biological family. The goal is to find the best home for the child. This is referred to as "the best interest of the child." It is a reminder that the focus is on the children and doing what is best on their behalf.

---

### QUESTION

1. When adopting a foster child, should the family treat the child like an adoptive child or a biological child? Is there a difference? Before going further into the case, answer that question from your perspective without reviewing the literature.

---

## THE CANNON ASSESSMENT

Helene arrived at the home of Larry and Caroline Cannon. Mrs. Cannon was an accountant for a small business, and Mr. Cannon was a manager for a lumber and supply company. The Cannons have been long-time foster parents, so a lot of the information Helene would need was already in their file. However, in this case, we will go through the process of collecting that information.

Adoption home studies include an assessment of the physical home—including space for the children, living conditions, and safety conditions—as well as the parents' reasons and motivation for wanting to adopt. Their ability to physically, emotionally, and financially provide for the children. What are the rules, beliefs and structure of the home? Family and friends support systems. Criminal background check, history of alcohol, substance abuse, or mental health issues. The parents will provide references and agree to attend orientation and training workshops. It takes several visits to gather that information and time to write the report, which is reviewed and approved by the adoption supervisor.

## SOCIAL HISTORY

Larry and Caroline Cannon married at the age of 18 shortly after graduating from high school. Larry started college, and the next year they had their first child. By the age of 21, they had three children. Now that Larry and Caroline have reached the age of 49, all three children are grown and moved out of the house.

After Larry graduated from college, they became foster parents. First infants, then younger sibling groups, and finally children of all ages and ethnicities. The caseworkers who worked with the Cannons were all positive about their commitment to the children, working with the agency and supporting the biological parents. The agency and community have recognized them for their commitment to foster care and providing a safe and secure home for children. Their compassion and commitment to family made them excellent at helping children in their care to return to their biological families or to move to an adoptive home. Children had success in their home and were able to thrive academically, mentally, behaviorally, and medically. They were open to meeting biological parents, providing updates and inviting them to the children's events. They also presented at foster parent trainings and provided support for other foster parents.

After 27 years as foster parents, Larry and Caroline decided the time was right to be adoptive parents. Attending the agency adoptive parent training, they were provided with resources to read, talked to adoptive parents, and they felt prepared to bring a child into their home permanently.

During one of the visits, Helene asked Larry and Caroline, "What behaviors by the foster children in your home did you find the most challenging?"

Throughout the interviews, Helene noticed that they were thoughtful in their answers. Never quick to answer but taking a moment to think about the question.

"The challenge came when we first took in older children," said Larry. "We wanted to believe that all children needed was love. We could provide a loving home, and the children would be fine. We had to understand their experiences and seeing them act out the things that people did to them. We had to adjust and accept that love was not enough, but a starting place."

"I think the thing that bothered me the most was not the fighting but the way the children would try and hurt each other. They did not fight over things; they battled over things. Moreover, they were little things to me, but the whole world to them. Like toys, food, or which chair someone was sitting in."

"How did you handle the fighting?"

"We learned to separate them, explaining the reasons why, and taking away the thing they were fighting over," said Larry. We also found ways to reward the child who did not start the fight. We wanted to discipline the wrong behaviors and reward good behaviors. In time we found that the children would fight less and less and started helping each other."

"Caroline, what behaviors did you find challenging?"

Caroline also paused before answering. "For me, it was the sexual abuse. That an adult would do that to a child, a baby, would still sicken me. I would see the children acting out sexual games, and I just wanted to hold them and say, 'that will never happen to you again.' It was going to the workshops and talking with other foster parents that helped me better understand why the children imitated those behaviors."

"If an adoptive child engaged in sexual acts, how would both of you handle that today?" asked Helene.

"Depending on the age, we would talk with them, show them other ways to play or address the anger they were feeling, and focus on rewarding new behaviors, and making that the center of our attention," said Caroline.

Larry agreed, adding, "It is easier to focus on what you should not be doing than on what you should be doing. Depending on the situation, we have learned on which one to place more attention. We have learned to address the behavior but focus on the positive."

Helene said, "Like foster care, adoption can put stress on the parents, family, and friends. What do your family and friends think about you adopting?"

"Our children, parents, siblings, and friends are all supportive of us adopting," said Caroline. "Our children would like for us to take a break and travel, but there are no other reservations."

"After 27 years, have you thought about taking a break?"

"We have taken breaks," said Larry. "We are very social and spend time with family and friends. We travel between children placed in our home, so we think there is a balance in our life."

"The last item I want to talk about is lifebooks," said Helene. She explained how the lifebooks contain pictures, letters, special items, and sometimes videos of family, friends, and special events. They keep the child connected to their past, to show there were positive people and things in their life, and they can carry that into their adoption. "We have parents who spend time with the child looking at and talking about what's in the lifebook. The child can add to the lifebook, and we ask parents to find opportunities to add their information to the lifebook to show the family expanding." The Cannons were happy to support the lifebook.

Helene completed her home study and approved the Cannons for adoption. The Cannons would attend a couple of additional workshops, and since they asked about adopting older children, she also wanted them to attend an adoptive parent support group.

# CHILD ADOPTION ASSESSMENT

When the termination hearing is set, the agency assigns an adoption worker to prepare the children for adoption, completes a child adoption assessment, works with the adoptive parents, makes the placement in the adoptive home, and supervises the adoptive placement for one year, at which time the adoption is finalized.

Calvin Quinn was assigned the case. Calvin had worked on several cases with his supervisor, but this was the first solo case. He read the foster care case several times to gain an understanding of what Curtis and William had experienced before foster care and in the foster care system. He would take the information from the file, and after talking with the foster care worker, start writing the child adoption assessment. As the case got closer to termination, he would meet with the boys and the foster parents. After the termination, he will try and meet with the biological parents to gather information on the family for the assessment. If the parents are willing to meet before the termination, he will start his assessment then. The foster care worker will let Calvin know when the biological parents are ready to meet.

## Child Assessment

The child adoption assessment serves several essential functions. First, it provides a permanent record for the child. It is a social history that includes information about the child's biological family; parents, siblings, relatives, and significant people in the child's life. It can tell the child where they came from and the places they lived. It can provide medical and psychological information to assist the adoptive parents and the child in adulthood with any health-related issues.

## Curtis and William Meet the Adoption Worker

Every child is different as they transition from foster care to adoption. Foster care always leaves the hope that they can go home. Adoption crushes that hope, with no real concept of what comes next. Most children believe that their parents don't want them, that they did something wrong or something is wrong with them. They can also believe that if your own family doesn't want you, why would any other family?

Curtis and William have a therapist, foster care worker, adoptive worker, and foster parents all helping them with the transition to adoption. The key is for these individuals to work together, playing different roles and developing the same message. The person they are going to be with over the next year is the adoption worker. This is also the person they and the boys have the most fragile relationship with. The person with the strongest relationship with the boys is going to be the conduit between the boys and the adoption worker.

In each meeting with Curtis and William, the foster care worker would talk about Calvin. He would share information, talk about his relationship with Calvin and the trust he has in him. The first meeting can take place anywhere, so they decide on one of the boys' favorite restaurant to eat and talk.

At the first meeting Calvin will ask questions to let the boys do most of the talking. Calvin will share a little about himself and let the boys ask any questions they want. The second meeting, all four of them meet again. The third meeting, Calvin meets with the boys at the foster home without the foster care worker. By meeting in the foster home, it still gives the boys a sense of security.

Calvin took over from the foster care worker helping the boys gather information for the lifebook. He assisted with finding information, pictures, and the boys writing stories. He used the lifebook as a way to talk about having a goodbye visit with their parents. He discussed what things they wanted to give their parents. The idea was their parents would never forget them and would hold on to those items and their memories. To help the boys remember their parents, he asked them what items they wanted from their parents.

The goodbye visit would be held at the agency. Some parents bring food or gifts for the children. Some parents bring relatives to say goodbye. Calvin's supervisor told him about cases where the parents did not want a goodbye visit, set a visit and did not show, or at the visit told the children not to love the adoptive parents, and they would continue to fight to get them back.

In most cases, while the parents were upset, they were supportive of the adoption in front of the children. Parents brought things for the lifebook, and most wrote a love letter to their children. If the parents brought food, sometimes they would include the adoption worker during the meal and other times they did not.

For Curtis and William, only the parents came for the goodbye visit. They brought pictures of the family, including relatives and friends, and a letter for each boy. They wanted the boys to know they would always be their parents, and one day they would see each other again. The parents and the boys cried and hugged each other.

When the visit was over, the foster care worker came into the room to stay with the boys, and Calvin walked out with the parents. He thanked them for all they were doing and said that if there was any information they needed, he would be happy to provide it. Calvin thanked them again, and they left.

Knowing Curtis and William would have a tough time after the visit, the foster parents were waiting in another room to take the boys home. Coming into the room, the foster parents hugged both boys and asked if they were ready to go. They helped them put everything into individual boxes and carried them to the car. The foster care worker told the foster parents to call him if there were any concerns.

After the termination, Calvin talked with the boys about adoption and the kind of family they wanted. At first, they did not have much to say about an adoptive family. When they did, they described an environment similar to their biological family. That was what they knew and wanted to go back to. Continuing the conversation, Calvin talked about the kind of family he wanted for them. He would use some of the descriptions that the boys used to apply to the family.

One of the techniques Calvin learned from his supervision was how to talk about adoption and to take the placement decision out of the hands of the adoptive families and into the adoption worker's hands. He also learned that children in these circumstances will think that no family wants them. When meeting a family, they are afraid they will say the wrong thing and that the family will not want them. Calvin sat with the boys to bring up the topic of selecting the right family.

"I am looking at families to find the right one for you," said Calvin. "People think the adoptive parents pick the children they want. I bet that is what you think."

The boys did not say anything, but their expression showed children who thought that was the case. They were taken out of their parents' home, lived in three different foster homes, and now an adoptive home. "Are you thinking that none of the homes you have been in wanted you?"

"I need you to know that my job and that of the foster care workers you have had is to protect you. My job is to find the best family for you. The adoptive families don't pick you; I pick them."

As if rehearsed, both boys looked up at him at the same time. They did not say anything but were waiting on his next words.

"Until I talk to a family about you, they don't know who you are. So they can't pick you or not pick you. We have talked about what you need in an adoptive home. I am sure there are other things you will tell me about what you want. I take that information and find a family that is right for you. I reject families that are not the right fit. I have worked with children where I had them visit a family. The children liked the family, but I could see it was not the right fit. So I say no to the family. I am here to help you. That will continue to be my promise to you. It is possible you may meet a few families, but until I find the right one, you will not move into that home."

"Do you understand what I am saying?" asked Calvin.

Both boys nodded their understanding.

"When will we meet a family?" asked Curtis.

"Soon. I am talking to some families, and soon you will get to visit with them. Once I have selected a family, I will tell you all about them, and you get to tell me what you think about them."

## ADOPTION PREPARATION

About 8 months after the completion of the home study, the agency contacted the Cannons about their interest in adopting sibling boys, Curtis Hall, age 12, and William Hall, age 11. They were two months from the termination hearing, and Calvin was looking through applications for potential families when he came across the Cannons'.

After reviewing the file and talking to the adoption recruiter and foster care worker, Calvin scheduled a meeting with the Cannons. The meeting is to share some information about the Halls and to get to know the Cannons. Calvin's assessment is to determine if he should continue working with the family regarding the Halls. Without using names, he shares information about the boys to gauge the interest of the Cannons. As he discusses the boys, he assesses if there are any concerns with the family or behaviors he thinks could be a challenge for them. Based on the information gathered, he believed they were ready to move to the next step.

The next step is scheduling a time for the Cannons to read Curtis and William's case file. The family comes to the agency to read the file because by policy it is not taken out of the agency. Depending on the length of the file, it can take several hours to read. Families may make a couple of visits to complete reviewing the file. The family can take notes as they read in order to ask questions about the case.

After reading the file and Calvin answering their questions, the Cannons felt they were ready for the next step: meeting the boys. Based on the questions asked and their understanding of the case, Calvin thought this could be a good match for the boys. The next steps were telling the boys about the Cannons and setting up the first meeting at the agency.

# THE VISITS

During several meetings, visits, and overnight stays, the Cannons felt they were ready to adopt Curtis and William. Larry and Caroline felt a connection with the boys. While they understand the challenges the boys had faced, they believed the one thing missing was permanency. From the abuse and neglect in the home, multiple moves, different foster homes, schools, and new rules to learn and follow, an adult would have a difficult time adjusting. Why would people think it would be easier for a child? They knew they could provide a safe care home, where the boys would feel protected and loved. They felt ready for this next phase of their lives.

Calvin wanted to make sure the Cannons were ready. Meeting with them, he asked, "You said Curtis and William are right for your home. They are also the only children presented to you. Is there a part of you that worries that if you said Curtis and William are not the right fit, it could be some time before we talk with you about other children?"

"I know you could think that way," said Caroline, "but that is not the case. We could read other cases and meet other children, but we know Curtis and William are the right children. I can't completely explain it, but there was a connection, and that tells us this is right for them and us."

Larry agreed with Caroline. As they talked, Calvin saw the passion and commitment for the boys. He could find nothing in their answers that would give him pause about making this placement.

In Calvin's conversations with the boys, William liked the family and was excited to move in, but most importantly, living with Curtis. Curtis was more reserved about the family. He was happy that William liked them, but he was not ready to invest in another relationship that would not last. Curtis told Calvin this home would not last because none of them had; why would this be any different? He would be ready for the next move. The boys moved into their home, and if everything were successful, in a year they would go to court and have the adoption finalized.

---

## QUESTIONS

1.  Review the literature on some of the topics covered in adoptive parent training, and list several of the main topics covered.

2.  Write an assessment of the Cannons. Use the literature to find an assessment tool you can use.

3.  Based on your assessment, what is the motivation for the Cannons wanting to be adoptive parents?

4.  Based on all the information you have gathered, discuss if you would place the Halls with the Cannons.

---

# THE CANNONS' HOME

With their experience as biological parents and foster parents, the Cannons were ready to be adoptive parents. They had talked about this with their adult children, siblings, and parents. While they did not receive the enthusiasm and excitement that they thought they would get from their family, in time they felt their family would be supportive of them adopting and grow to love the boys as much as they were growing to love them. When Curtis and William moved into the home, they had the option of sharing a bedroom or having separate bedrooms. William wanted them to share a bedroom, while Curtis wanted his own room. Because William was scared, Curtis agreed to share the bedroom with William until he was able to sleep alone.

The Cannons throw a house party to welcome the boys and invited family and friends to celebrate the new additions to the family. The Cannons' extended family were big on celebrations, and this was an opportunity to bring everyone together to continue their tradition.

At the party, Curtis felt uncomfortable around all the people. There was too much focus on him, with people asking lots of questions. He was trying to be on his best behavior, but the more people came around him, the more he thought he would explode. It was loud, and all he wanted was to be left alone. He could see William having a good time, and he did not want to mess it up for him. So he pretended to have fun and laughed when they laughed.

William loved the people, music, noise, and most importantly, the attention. They wanted to know his favorite game, TV show, song, color, toy, comic book, anything he wanted to share with them. They laughed when he said something funny and hugged him when he said something sweet. For that evening, he did not think about his family, all the moves, or his brother. He enjoyed his spotlight.

## The Adjustment of Curtis and William

At first, both boys were on their best behavior. They followed all of the rules, participated in family activities, and attended their counseling sessions. As the weeks turned into a month, there were slight changes in their behavior and disposition. William started asking when they could see his parents. As the therapist and the adoption worker tried to explain the termination of parental rights and why he would not see their parents again, William became more silent and withdrawn.

With the move to another home and another school, there was also the change from the foster care worker to the adoption worker. So the boys had a new person they had to interact with and talk about how things were going. The one consistent person was the therapist; she did not change from the foster care placement to the adoptive placement.

Everyone noticed that while William brought his biological parents up in conversation, Curtis never asked about them, brought them up in conversation, or answered questions when asked about them. Most of his answers were "I don't remember"; "I don't know"; or "why do you keep asking me about them?" As time went by, Curtis became more silent, not only about his biological parents but about other topics as well. He did not want to talk about his friends, places he had lived, or any of the issues in the home. He did not play with the other children in the neighborhood, and he would spend the day sitting in his room, on the front porch, or in the backyard. He did interact with his brother, and there were never any signs that he was still mad at William for talking to Mr. Kevin. He liked comic books, and he would spend his time reading and rereading the comic books he had collected. The Cannons would take him to the comic book shop to pick out comics, and that was one of the few times that Curtis would talk. He would explain who the comic book characters were, the powers they had, and the villains they were fighting. The Cannons noticed that Curtis did like to read, so they also went to the library to find books on topics that he was interested in. The fantasy books came closest to the comic books, and those were the books Curtis read.

Toward the end of summer, Curtis's behavior became more disruptive. The therapist noticed that the behaviors he had exhibited in the previous foster homes were starting to appear in the adoptive home. The therapist described it as Curtis holding all his emotions in as he was waiting for the next move to a new family. He held them for as long as he could but had gotten to the breaking point where he could no longer hold them in. Because Curtis would not talk about what was going on, the therapist had to assess from working with other children that Curtis was trying to contain the feelings, emotions, and behaviors that he had, and in trying to keep them under control that he was slowly boiling over.

Calvin had talked to the Cannons about this possibility of a boiling point. The boys had been in a state of uncertainty, thanks to all of the moves and adjustments. Not knowing how people would react to them, the boys were trying to manage all those feelings without the safety of knowing the future. They kept a lot of things bottled up. They could not control all of their frustrations, nor were they ready to fully express their happiness publicly only to be disappointed.

In the Cannon home, the boys were experiencing a sense of security and stability. They were told this was their last move. It was hard for the boys to believe, but as things started to settle, everything they had been holding in was finally coming out—all of the frustration, anger, sense of not belonging; parents who did not want them; Mr. Kevin, who told on them; the foster care workers and foster families that did not want them; and now a new family, school, adoption worker. They were approaching the point where they could no longer control all that was turning inside of them. That boiling point came one day when the Cannons talked about going to the park, and Curtis started yelling at them.

"Why do you want me to go to the park? What do you want from me?" Then he looked at them and said, "You are not my parents. I don't know where my parents are, but you won't let me see them."

It was the first time since he was adopted that he brought up his biological parents. From that point on Curtis fought with the Cannons about getting up in the morning, eating his breakfast, doing his reading, and studying for school. When disciplined, he acted like it didn't make a difference. If he was sent to his room or not allowed to read or watch television, Curtis would sit there quietly. Once the punishment was over, he would begin arguing and disagreeing with the Cannons again. When the family went to church, community events, children's activities, or over to a relative's house, Curtis had a difficult time getting along with people. If there were children around who were bigger or smaller than him, he would get into a pushing match or fight with them. As the Cannons observed, Curtis could be on one side of the room with a child on the other side of the room, and he would walk across the room, push the child down, then walk back without saying a word.

William was not as disruptive as Curtis. He did have some challenging behavior problems, and he had more difficulty learning than Curtis, but he was not prone to get into fights. As time went on, William grew more introverted. At first, he would ask about his parents every day, drawing pictures of them with himself between them holding hands and wanting to visit them. Each time he got the same answer, that he could not visit them or talk to them, he would get mad and start crying. Over time he asked about them less, and he didn't draw as many pictures of them as he had in the past. As the summer drew to an end, he became more fidgety, agitated, and quick to respond when someone said something and was constantly moving around the house. It looked like something inside him was trying to get out but was unable to, and the constant moving was a way to try and get it out of him.

The Cannons attended Sunday school and church with Curtis and William. At first, the boys seemed to enjoy Sunday school. However, over time both boys would push other children, take their pencils, crayons, or books, and if someone said something, they would yell at them. The Cannons were asked to take the boys out of Sunday school because they were too disruptive to the other children. Therefore, the Cannons stopped attending adult Sunday school, and the family just went to church together. However, it was difficult for the boys to stay in their seats. They were fidgety, saying things out loud, making comments or noises, and would not stay quiet during the service. Teenagers and adults in the church offered to watch the boys, together or to split them up and sit in different parts of the church, but that only worked for a few weeks, and then the boys began engaging in the same behaviors as before. While parishioners tried to be supportive of the Cannons, they were becoming more frustrated with the behavior of the boys and the inability of the Cannons to control those behaviors.

## School

When the school term started, Curtis and William would attend a new school. Part of Calvin's job is to help prepare the teachers for the new children coming to school. His supervisor told him of stories where the teacher would introduce the new students as adoptive children, tell how the children got to their school, and mentioned a few times where the teacher talked about the abuse the children suffered. Today, they work with the school social worker to let the teachers know about the children and what they can say. If the school does not have a counselor or social worker, the adoption worker will meet with the teacher to go over what they should say and not say about the children. The supervisor said this has helped the children adjust and fit into the new environment. The children would meet their teachers, the principal, and the social worker before school started.

For Curtis and William, they were adjusting to an adoption worker, a new family, and a new school. We know that children thrive in a stable environment, but what the boys were learning was anything but stability. They knew how to pack quickly, try not to leave anything, learn new rules, new family, new names, new streets, schools, and new social workers for them to tell the same stories over and over. They knew they were not wanted, and they would keep moving until they were grown. What they did not know was whether they would have each other.

When school started, the challenging behaviors continued. There were multiple timeouts, visits to the principal's office and the counselor's office, and multiple calls for the parents to come and talk to the boys or to take them home and try again the next day.

While their jobs gave them some flexibility, the Cannons knew if they missed too many days of work their employers would not be happy. They no longer had the foster care worker who could go to the school when there was a problem. Curtis and William were their children, and when a problem arose, it was their responsibility to handle it. After missing several days of work to go to school to check on the boys, their employers told them that they would have to take vacation days in the future.

Caroline Cannon would talk to her sisters and mother about the boys' behavior and asked them for any ideas of what they could do. At first, she found her sisters and mother helpful; they would take the boys out or come to the house so she could get out. However, one day she was shocked when her sisters and mother came to the house and said they should return the children to the agency because they were causing too much stress on the family. Caroline believed her family would support their decision to adopt, even if there were some challenges with the boys. The family knew where the boys came from and the kinds of abuse that they had experienced before moving into their home. She could not believe that her family was not more understanding and sympathetic to the plight of her children and her need to support the boys and help them deal with all the abuse and trauma they had experienced.

Talking to some friends with whom she had grown up, Caroline again was surprised to hear the same recommendation, that the children should go back to the agency. Caroline thought she would never tell any of them to give up their children and she couldn't see why they would say that to her. Over time she found herself more isolated from her family and friends. They appeared to be uninvited to friends' events and parties, especially if the party included bringing children. At family gatherings, the family members would ask if there was someone else who could watch the boys while they came over to the house.

As Caroline found herself more alone and isolated from friends and family, her frustration turned to rejection and then to anger.

When Calvin met with the Cannons, they talked about some of their frustration with their families. Calvin had given them information on adoptive parent support groups, but they had not attended any meetings. When Calvin asked why they had not attended any meetings, it was difficult to get a straight answer from them. They kept focusing on that their families would come around and support them.

"Why do you believe they will come around?" asked Calvin.

"Because we are family, and we have always been there for each other and our children," said Caroline.

"Do you see your adopted children the same way you see your biological children?'

"Of course, we do," said Caroline. "There is no difference. Why, do people think there is?"

"Who thinks the two are different?" asked Calvin.

"I have noticed my sisters do not treat Curtis and William like they did my other children. I have asked them why, but I can't get a good answer."

"What do you think the reasons are for the difference?" asked Calvin.

Larry and Caroline sat quietly for a long time before answering.

Larry spoke first. "I don't think they truly understand that there is no difference between the two. Family is family, however they come together."

"For some families, blood is the most important thing. Curtis and William are not blood."

"But they are family. You would think they would understand that and be supportive of us. We are family," said Caroline.

Calvin remembered the conversation about this topic with his supervisor, who said that for some families, no matter how many times you bring up the subject, they believe their family will do the right thing and love their children as they do. However, every family is different, and they may not see the children the same way. Now Calvin is sitting here, waiting for it play out. He had talked with them about this topic, but his supervisor was right. People believe what they want to believe.

"When families are not as supportive as we would like, there are adoptive parent support groups that can help," said Calvin. "They are going through some of the same family issues that you are."

"We don't need support groups," said Caroline. "We know how to take care of our children."

The supervisor told Calvin that there is a debate over whether you should treat the child like an adoptive child or a biological child. People go both ways, and there is nothing wrong with either approach. The issue is to whom people turn for help. For some families, when they say you treat the child as a biological child, they mean that you would not seek outside help for your biological child. If you seek outside help for your adoptive child, you are not a real parent. They don't want people saying the child is not theirs. Therefore, they will not attend support groups or parenting classes or turn to adoptive parents for help.

For other families, when they say treat the child like an adoptive child, it means they will seek outside help. They understand that their family may not be able to provide the type of support they need, and adoptive families dealing with the same issues would be better support.

The challenge for Calvin was how to get the Cannons to see the benefit of outside help. He has learned that when families feel isolated, it increases the chances of an adoptive disruption. He did not want that for Curtis and William. They had enough moves in their short lives, and they did not need another move.

## QUESTIONS

1. Now that you have completed the case and reviewed the literature, let's go back to this question: when you adopt a foster child, should the family treat the child like an adoptive child or a biological child? Explain why your original opinion has stayed the same or changed.

2. How can a child learn to build relationships, stability, and consistency in adulthood if they have not learned those skills as children?

3. Calvin referenced an adoption disruption. What is an adoption disruption? There are also adoption dissolutions. Explain what that is.

4. This family is at a central point in their relationship. Discuss a few intervention strategies you would use with the family.

5. How might Curtis use the system model with the Cannons to clarify the role of a support group? To discuss the impact of the lack of support from biological kin?

## REFERENCES

Carnochan, S., Moore, M., & Austin, M. J. (2013, May). Achieving timely adoption. *Journal of Evidence-Based Social Work*. https://doi.org/10.1080/15433714.2013.788950

Child Welfare Information Gateway (https://www.childwelfare.gov/pubPDFs/s_disrup.pdf)

Coakley, J. F., & Berrick, J. D. (2008). Research review: In a rush to permanency: Preventing adoption disruption. *Child and Family Social Work, 13*(1), 101–112. https://doi.org/10.1111/j.1365-2206.2006.00468.x

Crea, T. M., Barth, R. P., & Moreno, H. M. (2012). Consistency between self-reported risks and strengths among prospective adoptive couples: Findings from home studies. *Child Welfare, 91*(4), 109–126.

Denby, R. W., Alford, K. A., & Ayala, J. (2011). The journey to adopt a child who has special needs: Parents' perspectives. *Children and Youth Services Review, 33*(9), 1543–1554. https://doi.org/10.1016/j.childyouth.2011.03.019

Gates, G. J., Badgett, M. V. L., Macomber, J. M., & Chambers, K. (2007). *Adoption and foster care by lesbian and gay parents in the United States. The Williams Institute, UCLA School of Law* (pp. 1–43). https://doi.org/10.1037/e690872011-001

Goldman, G. D. L., & Ryan, S. D. (2011). Direct and modifying influences of selected risk factors on children's pre-adoption functioning and post-adoption adjustment. *Children and Youth Services Review, 33*(2), 291–300. https://doi.org/10.1016/j.childyouth.2010.09.012

Groza, V., & Ryan, S. D. (2002). Pre-adoption stress and its association with child behavior in domestic special needs and international adoptions. *Psychoneuroendocrinology, 27*(1–2), 181–197. https://doi.org/10.1016/S0306-4530(01)00044-0

Houston, D. M., & Kramer, L. (2008). Meeting the long-term needs of families who adopt children out of foster care: A three-year follow-up study. *Child Welfare, 87*(4), 145–170.

Horwitz, S. M., Hurlburt, M. S., Goldhaber-Fiebert, J. D., Palinkas, L. A., Rolls-Reutz, J., Zhang, J., ... Landsverk, J. (2014). Exploration and adoption of evidence-based practice by US child welfare agencies. *Children and Youth Services Review, 39*, 147–152. https://doi.org/10.1016/j.childyouth.2013.10.004

Hussey, D. L., Falletta, L., & Eng, A. (2012). Risk factors for mental health diagnoses among children adopted from the public child welfare system. *Children and Youth Services Review, 34*(10), 2072–2080. https://doi.org/10.1016/j.childyouth.2012.06.01

Lockwood, K. K., Friedman, S., & Christian, C. W. (2015). Permanency and the foster care system. *Current Problems in Pediatric and Adolescent Health Care, 45*(10), 306–315. https://doi.org/10.1016/j.cppeds.2015.08.005

McDonald, T., Press, A., Billings, P., & Moore, T. (2007). Partitioning the adoption process to better predict permanency. *Child Welfare, 86*(3), 5–32.

Orsi, R. (2015). Predicting re-involvement for children adopted out of a public child welfare system. *Child Abuse and Neglect, 39*, 175–184. https://doi.org/10.1016/j.chiabu.2014.10.005

# CHAPTER 4

# Inside My Head

## First 24 Hours, A Residential Placement

*George Grant, Jr.*

## INTRODUCTION

This case, regarding two siblings, a girl and a boy, and their placement in a residential facility is different from most cases you read because you will have access to information that generally you would not have for your treatment planning. The focus of this case study is to experience a foster care journey through the eyes of a teenager. Throughout the case, she is thinking about what is happening to her, trying to make sense of her circumstances and the struggles a child has in foster care trying to find their place. We believe this journey will help you understand some of the things children think about but do not share with you. Let's follow the journey of Cori Woodall through her mind.

## CHILD WELFARE

The two words *child welfare* are polysemic in the number of meanings. One must be clear about what aspect of child welfare one refers to and for what cause. From prenatal care, infant care, sudden infant death syndrome, feeding, health, child development, physical, developmental, educational, environmental exposure, child abuse, neglect, foster care, juvenile detention, medical, social skills, mentoring, safe place, music, sports, adult involvement, laws, systems, relationships positive and negative, what family you are born into, what ZIP code you are born into, etc., are all subcategories of child welfare.

  As a therapist, when you meet a client for the first time, you may have a file with one sheet of paper or 100 sheets of paper regarding that person (for children with a long history of involvement with the child welfare system, the hard copies can fill not just a folder, but boxes of records). The information given to you will become the foundation for the part of child welfare with which you will interact.

One crucial aspect of the foster care system is where a child will live. While the general term is foster care placement, it encompasses a number of different settings. A child in foster care could stay with their biological parents, relatives, friends, a foster home, group home, juvenile facility, or a residential placement. The main purpose of these placements is to provide protection and stability, and where treatment can be provided to address the issues that brought the child to foster care. Foster care placements are listed from least restrictive to most restrictive. Staying in the biological home is least restrictive, while juvenile detention is the most restrictive. A residential facility is considered just below the most restrictive. These can be locked facilities, which means the outside doors open into the facility, but a key or passcode is required to leave the facility. There is debate over whether facilities should be locked from the inside, and the law or belief of the facility will determine if it is locked.

## QUESTIONS

1. Define residential care.
2. What are some of the ways a residential placement can create an environment where children can feel safe, work on the issues that brought them there, and address the trauma of being in that setting?
3. How would you help the children find structure, order, and predictability in a residential placement when most of their lives have been unstructured?
4. Review the professional literature and develop a code of conduct with five key points for residential facilities.

Residential facilities will accept children by age, gender, behavioral issues, mental health needs, specialized medical care, or a disability requiring certain structures for easier access and movement. These placements can have bedrooms for one to four children per room. There are also general areas where the children come together for meals, meetings, and group activities. They are staffed 24 hours a day and never close. Most residential facilities also provide services for children who are not part of the foster care system.

## QUESTIONS

1. Find a children's residential facility in your community.
2. Discuss its mission and goals.

3. Provide demographics of children in the facility.
4. What types of services do they provide?
5. Review their annual report to find the outcomes for the services they provide.

---

## CORI WOODALL

It's my second day in residential, and I'm walking down the hall to meet another therapist. Mary, a caseworker, is walking beside me. (Maybe she thinks I will make a run for the exit.) As Mary talks, I know she is preparing me for my meeting with the therapist. This is not my first time—just another person to ask me about my childhood, what happened to my parents, how I feel about that, what I want out of life, and, of course, the big question: why do I think I'm here? At 13, I have had enough therapy to know what I need to say and what they want to hear.

"You can trust me," they all say, but trust gets you moved from house to house, new families that may not want you, people thinking you are crazy, and people who want to save you. I have learned to tell people what they want to hear, but not to trust them. Anyway, you can't trust people you don't know. And you *definitely* can't trust people you do know.

Mary knocks on the door, and I hear a woman's voice on the other side telling me to come in. Opening the door, Mary and I walk into the office. The only person in the room is a Black woman standing in front of me. I have had a lot of therapists, but this is the first time that I've had a Black woman. With a slight smile on her face, she walks over to me, reaching out her hand to shake mine.

She says, "Good morning, my name is Linda Sampson. It is nice to meet you. Thank you for coming to meet with me this morning."

Like I had a choice. I shake her hand briefly, but I don't say anything. She looks at Mary and says thank you. Mary looks at me and says she will be back in 45 minutes and then turns and leaves the room.

The office is small but not cramped, with a bookshelf behind the desk and a table with two chairs sitting by a window. She asks me if I want to sit down, and I take the chair closest to me. Instead of saying my name, she asks what my name is. I say, "Cori Woodall." She repeats my name and takes the other chair at the table.

I notice no large folders of information about me sitting on the table or the desk. I am used to sitting down with people opening my file and reading off the information we both already know. I always feel like they've already made up their mind about me. I know what they are going to say, and they know what I'm going to say because of all the information right there. That file—with every bad thing my family and I have ever done—will follow me for the rest of my life.

Everyone I meet tells me the rules: what I can and can't do, the rewards I can get if my behavior is good and the punishments if my behavior is inappropriate. They never say *bad*; it's always *inappropriate*. I've heard it so many times that I could sit in the other chair and say it to myself. So, I sit and wait for the show to start.

Linda's first question was to ask how my brother was doing. I was ready to give the same response I do whenever they ask me how I'm doing and how I'm adjusting to this place. I was taken aback when she started with my brother. That was so strange that I wanted to know if something had happened to him. Since we came in yesterday evening, I was sent to the girls' side, and he went to the boys' side. I have not seen him. I asked if he is okay. She responded that he is, and she was sorry she had asked the question that way.

She then looked at me or inside me because I can feel what she was going to say, but it was something I had not heard before.

She said, "As the big sister I bet you've been the one taking care of and protecting your brother most of his life?"

I almost answered too quickly but caught myself at the last second. I wanted to say yes, I've been the one looking out for him when no one else had, especially all the adults who were supposed to care for him. However, I did not say that because I didn't want him to seem weak.

So instead I said, "We look out for each other, and that's the way it's always been." I didn't know how much we would be separated from each other, and I didn't want them to have a negative perception of my brother as weak.

Linda said, "I understand, and the fact that you haven't seen your brother since you came is wrong."

She then went over to her phone and told someone to bring my brother to her office. She sat back down and said, "Before we continue, why don't you and your brother spend some time catching up?"

"Unfortunately, I need to be in the room, but it will give you a chance to reconnect, and I'll do my best not to listen to your conversation."

Inside I am excited to check on my brother. However, on the outside, I keep the same demeanor. I don't want her to think that she was doing me a favor, or that I owe her because I got to see him. So instead I'll act like it's no big deal, but I had to think about how I was going to react when Raymond walked through that door with her sitting there.

While we were waiting, she did not ask me any questions about my past. She talked mostly about herself. How long she had worked here, where she was born, some of the things she enjoyed doing, and how she became a therapist. I listened but kept quiet.

Finally, her question for me was what I wanted to do after I graduated from high school. I had been asked about high school numerous times, but it was the way she framed it. It was not *if* I graduated from high school, but *when* I graduated from high school. Conversations in the past were always about how my behavior would prevent me from graduating. I would have to get a GED or suffer the consequences that happen to high school dropouts. However, Linda framed it in a way that graduating from high school was a given, not my past, not my behavior, not what I needed to change, but just the simple question of what I wanted to do when I graduated from high school.

I did not have an answer because I never really thought that far ahead. It's one of those rich-people questions, you know? I had enough to deal with every day, I have only thought about not being in foster care, where my brother and I would have someplace to live where we could take care of each other and not depend on anyone else. How we would live, I don't have an answer. I just know I want to be 18 so I don't have to deal with any of these people anymore and no one can tell me what to do. I just want my brother and me to be free. I know that does not sound like much, but right now that is my world. To be free from all the adults who control our lives, telling us what to do, where to live, move us from one side of the state to another side of the state, to keep starting over with people we don't know, places we have never been or heard of, but yet somehow figuring out how to adjust to all of this and not get into trouble. I get tired of thinking about it.

## RAYMOND

There was a knock on the door, and Linda said to come in. The door opened, and Raymond was standing there in front of me. He was next to a man that must be the same as Mary but on the boys' side of the building. Linda said thank you, and the man touched Raymond's shoulder, turned, walked out, and closed the door.

First, I just sat there and looked at him. In just one day he looked smaller to me. I got out of my chair, and he ran over and hugged me. We just stood there for a long time as he held me as tight as he could. I held onto him, and no words were exchanged. I could hear from his breathing that he was crying just a little bit. I pulled him away and wiped the tears from his eyes and then held him again.

Finally, I heard Linda's voice saying that we could sit down. I turned to face her, and she came up to us and held out her hand for Raymond. She introduced herself and thanked him for coming. I found it odd she was thanking him as she thanked me when I knew we had to come if she said so. I had my hand around Raymond's shoulder as he reached out his hand to shake Linda's. She explained who she was and that I had asked if we could spend time together.

She said, "The visit has to be in the office, and I can't leave, but I will move the chairs around so you can sit together and talk while I sit at my desk."

I noticed the way she had the chairs seated; our backs were to hers. I wondered why that was. Was there some trick or some way for her to hear or see what we were doing by pretending like she was not? I was not sure, but I paid attention to see if I could figure it out.

I asked Raymond how he was doing, and at first, he just said fine, and then quickly added, "I miss you. I don't know why they can't put us together in the same room."

I tried to explain why the boys are on one side and the girls on the other, and even though we were family that was the rule in the center. I did tell him that I would try to see if we could spend more time together and play some of the games we love. A small smile came over his face, and he held my hand just a little bit tighter. I turned to look at Linda to see what she would say, but she did not look up and continued with whatever she was working on. I did not know if she heard us, or was pretending not to hear us, but she never joined in the conversation.

I wondered how he was doing on the boys' side. He's a nice person who cares about people and always tries to do good. I feared that the other boys would take advantage of that and he would not know how to protect himself. I need to find a way to remind him of some of the things we talked about in other places we lived. I love the fact that I could hold his hand and sit with him, and the hug that he gave me, but I don't think it would be a good idea to do that in public. People need to see Raymond as strong so they will not take advantage of him. If he comes across as too emotional and excited, I know kids will see that as a weakness. I am unsure how to address this, but I must keep thinking about ways to protect him.

He asked me how long we were going to be in this place, and I told him I didn't know. I turned and looked at Linda and asked her if she knew how long we were going to be here. Linda came around her desk and stood at the table in front of us. She said that the plan was for us to learn the skills necessary to leave here and be placed together in an adoptive family.

Raymond looked at her and said, "We already are a family, and I don't want to be separated from my sister."

Linda looked at both of us, replying that was her goal, to find a family for both of us so that we would be together.

There was something about Linda when I first came in that I liked just a little bit. It could be the fact that she did not have the file in front of her, or that she asked about my brother and then brought him in for a visit. But all of that started fading away when she talked about an adoptive family. It was not the first time we heard that, and I knew it would not be the last. We had been told many times how difficult it is to find someone who would take both of us at our ages. Who knew being 13 and 10 years old were too old?

While I wanted to keep Raymond near me, I knew he needed a family. My goal has been how to separate us, so he could get adopted while people wanted him. Because he was a good person and only 10, I felt there were families out there that would take him, but at 13, I did not see any families who would be interested in me, and I was not sure that I wanted to be part of another family.

---

**QUESTIONS**

1. Review in your state the number of children eligible for adoption. Breaking that data down by age, race, and gender, describe those children.
2. Which children are the most difficult for which to find adoptive homes?
3. Is there any data to support Cori's belief that it is harder to find adoptive homes for older children?
4. Review the literature on older siblings having to parent younger siblings. What does the research tell us about these relationships?
5. What does the research say about how successful these adoptive placements are when the older sibling is replaced by the adult parent to parent the younger child?
6. Based on what Cori is thinking, does she want Raymond and her adopted together or Raymond adopted by himself? Discuss your reasoning.

---

Some of my behaviors were being mad at people over my life, the ways that I was treated, and others were for people to see that if we were separated, Raymond could get a family. At the same time, I didn't want Raymond to think that I don't want him or want to be with him, so I need the agency to separate us instead of me. I had said to the previous therapist that it was fine to separate us, so Raymond could get a family. But I never said that in front of Raymond. His sense of family is only with me, with our parents dead, and there were very few relatives we had much contact with. He always looked at family as the two of us, and I just can't bear for him to think that I don't want him.

## NOW THE THERAPY STARTS

After Raymond left, Linda moved the chairs back to their original positions and sat down at the table. Instead of focusing on how I was feeling, Linda focused on how I thought Raymond was feeling. She wanted to know when she met with him later today if there was anything I wanted her to focus on. That surprised me again, and I wondered if this was a trick or some way to get me to talk by using my brother in this way. I didn't know what to think, but I did know that I was going to be careful what I said. I didn't want to give her any information that she could use against my brother. I don't know what she knows about us and what her opinion is of us. I know from dealing with other workers, I think they just see us as damaged kids who are not that smart, would get into trouble, and are not capable of taking care of ourselves. Like we had a choice!

We talked a little bit more about Raymond, and I did share that he is a nice person. But sometimes he lets people take advantage of him, and that is how he gets into trouble. She then asked me what they could do to help Raymond and to make his time here more comfortable. I say that I want to spend more time with him, and I think that would make him feel comfortable and secure.

"We have moved around a lot, so he does not get a chance to make friends." As I talked, all the conversation was about Raymond, but I felt like I was talking about me.

Linda then shifted the conversation to the residential facility. She talked about some of the rules and policies, who the people were, and how they were there to help me. She then asked if I had any questions or was there anything that I wanted to talk about. At this point, I did not because I had been through this before. I knew the rules, even though every place was a little different; in the end, not much changes.

For some reason, I wondered if this is the point she would ask me about the death of my parents. I don't cry when I talk about them, but I have found that the therapist seems to be happier when you cry. There have been times that I pretended to cry, and I didn't have to answer as many questions.

Time did go by fast because before I knew it there was a knock at the door. Mary came in, and Linda stood up and reached out her hand to shake mine. I then followed Mary out of the office back to my bedroom. Mary said I could relax, and she would be back to talk about the activities for today.

### QUESTIONS

1. Based on the information you have gathered to this point, write a two-page assessment of Cori.
2. Identify what trauma you believe Cori has experienced from your assessment.
3. Use the literature to find examples of children's opinions regarding living in residential facilities.

## WAITING FOR DINNER

I have spent a lot of time alone, but there are times that cause me to think about things I don't want to think about. I think part of feeling alone is all the moving we have done. We moved when Mom and Dad were alive, and then we moved after they died. I can remember more than Raymond can, and I wonder when he has questioned me how much I should tell him and how much I should keep to myself. I do get tired of keeping it to myself. However, I do not trust the people around me, and I am never sure what people are going to do with the information. I want my brother to get adopted, but are people going to think he is weird or strange because he has not lived the kind of life that most kids have lived? He is the kid of dead parents. Sometimes I lose count of the number of places we lived, the number of names we were supposed to remember, and the same questions asked over and over.

The question everyone wants to know is, how did my parents die? They know my mother killed my father with a gun. When I heard the shot, I ran to their bedroom to see my father lying on the floor with blood all around him. I froze at the door, unable to say a word. He was not moving, but the blood around him kept spreading.

*Stop thinking about that.*

I can't.

If only I hadn't frozen. If I could have said one word, maybe I could have saved him. But I could not speak. And in my silence, I killed my mother. If I could have said one word, she would not have put the gun to her head and pulled the trigger. Why did I not help her? What is wrong with me, I ask myself over and over? One word. I could not say one word. I never told Raymond I saw what happened because I don't want him to be mad at me. He would ask me, what did I do? What would I say? I stood there watching them both on the floor, their blood pooling together, and I did nothing to stop the bleeding. I could have gotten towels, talked to them, or called for help. I was told our neighbor heard the shots and called the police. Raymond was in our bedroom sleeping and did not hear a thing. When the police came, they found me standing at the bedroom door. They tried talking to me, asking what happened, and if I was all right. Why should I talk now? I didn't when I could have saved them.

I have never told anyone I saw what happened. Months later, when I did tell them, I said I heard gunshots, went to the bedroom, and they were lying on the floor. "Did you see what happened?" they would ask. To this day I have always said, "No."

I don't want to think about what happened. Why can't I think about something good? What is wrong with me?

I have Raymond, and that's the thing that keeps me going. I sometimes wonder if Raymond was not around if I would run away from these places, or would I be better off like my parents are now? I have thought of all the ways I could kill myself. Is Raymond my excuse not to do it, not knowing how he would react if I were dead? He would be alone, and there would be no one to protect him. I also wondered if I killed myself, would he think it was okay for him to do the same thing? Maybe he is my excuse to do it. If I am gone, he would be better off.

Why do I have these thoughts? I am so tired, and my head hurts all the time. I don't know what to do or whom to talk to. Why did my parents do this to me? I feel isolated and trapped. The things that I have no control over have taken control of my life. Sometimes I still wonder if I could have stopped Mom from killing Dad. Was he that bad a person? I don't remember him as bad. I thought he cared about us. I can remember him chasing me around the house and tickling me until I cried with laughter. I remember kisses on the forehead before going to sleep. Why can't I remember the bad things that would make my mother kill him?

Without asking those questions to my therapists, they would tell me, "You could not have done anything to help them. You had no control over what was happening, and you are the child, they were the adults, and there was nothing you could have done."

I know they are telling me that to make me feel better, but all it does is let me know what little control I have over my life. Because I could not do anything, it resulted in Raymond and me moving from place to place, some nice people, some not-so-nice people, new rules, new expectations, new ways of talking, dressing, eating, living, getting up in the morning, and going to bed at night because I did not have any control. What has changed?

There are schools where people know that you are in foster care and they tease you. They say things like you don't have any parents, or you don't have anyone who cares about you. The worst is when they say your parents killed themselves so they didn't have to live with you.

Most of the time I could let that go, but then somebody would pick on Raymond, and I hate it when people pick on him. I have not told people that most of my fights were not about people picking on me, it was them making fun of Raymond. I told one worker that early in one of our moves but afterward I felt like I should not have said anything. I wondered if people knew that I was getting in fights over Raymond they would separate us, and I would be unable to protect him anymore. They would probably think if they separated us, I would have no reason to fight anymore. And maybe that is true; I have no idea. I do know that I have been the only constant person in his life, and I just don't know what those other adults would do. Mommy kills Daddy in front of me and then kills herself in front of me, and those are supposed to be the people who love me. Why would adults who do not know me want to help me?

I do hope there is a place for Raymond. That there is a family that will accept him and make him part of their family. If that could happen, then I would not have to worry so much about him. But I don't know if that will happen if they keep trying to adopt us together. Maybe he would be better off if I was not here. But what if I was gone and they still could not find an adoptive family for him? He would move from place to place alone. I wish my head would stop hurting.

For these sets of questions, review the professional literature on teenagers and suicide.

1. What are the major causes of suicide for teenagers in the foster care system?
2. Discuss some of the warning signs you should look out for concerning teenage suicide.
3. Should you ask teens about suicide if they have not brought up the subject to you?
4. Does asking a teen about suicide increase the risk that they will attempt suicide?
5. Discuss why you think Cori blames herself for her parents' death.
6. What were the ages of Cori and Raymond when their parents died? What impact do their ages have on their development?
7. What are several questions to ask teenagers at risk of suicide?

## THAT EVENING

That evening everyone on the boys' and the girls' sides came together for dinner. I started talking to a couple of girls I was walking in with. Although the boys and girls were separated for breakfast and lunch, we could sit together at dinner. Looking around the room, you could see some of the people who had been there a long time by the way they interacted with each other. I could also see the quiet group of kids who sat by themselves and stayed out of people's way. As one of the new people in the room, I could tell that some people were looking at me, trying to figure out who I am. They do not know why I am here, but news travels fast, so they will know by tomorrow.

From previous group homes and residential facilities, I knew that there would be a group of people who would want to test me. Even in these settings, there are hierarchies of those in charge and those who do the bidding of those in charge.

I found that kids fell into three groups. The largest group was the followers, kids who did what they were told and did not want to cause trouble, and so they never bothered those kids who were in charge. The second group was the kids in charge, the leaders, the ones who could bully and push people around and tell them what to do. The last group was the group that nobody bothered; they were talked about as the crazy kids, the strange kids, or the kids that you never knew what would happen if they went off. Those kids were left alone, and they did not belong to any group. So, as the new person, people wanted to see which of the three groups I belonged to.

I learned early on that the third group was the best group to be part of. You got into trouble with the adults, and there were punishments that you had to receive, but it also put you in a position where the leaders and the followers left you alone. You may have some confrontations with the leaders, but it only takes a couple of times for them to move on to someone else. Over the years, I found that the leader group did not intimidate me because I never backed down.

I saw Raymond coming through the door on the opposite side of the room. He was looking around nervously, trying to figure out what was going on and where to go. As I stood there watching him, his eyes met mine. Within a few seconds, he was moving quickly across the room until he got to me and gave me a big hug. While I wrapped my arms around him, there was a part of me that wished he had not done that. We did not know these kids yet, and my concern was he was showing weakness. I could not push him away, but I would have a conversation with him later and remind him of what we had talked about in the past about how to interact with each other when other people were around. But I also had to remember that he was 10, scared, and I was his big sister.

We went through the line, got our food, and sat together. Raymond talked about his day and the kinds of things that he was involved with. It sounded like people treated him decently and he got along with the kids that he met today.

For new kids, there's a school within the residential facility. Those who are successful and not causing a lot of problems get to leave the residential facility during the day and go to regular school. We both would start the residential school tomorrow, and Raymond was concerned that he would be behind the other kids.

After dinner, kids could play games, watch television, or watch a movie. Raymond and I decided to sit off by ourselves and talk. Raymond talked about the long car ride to get to this place. When I was walking with Mary to meet Linda, I asked her how long the car ride was to this place. She said it was almost 3 hours. I can remember Raymond looking out the window and watching all of the buildings and houses disappear. Although we have been in a lot of different settings, we have always been in the same city. So, while we may not have been in a particular part of town, there were always streets that told us how to get back to where we used to live. But riding in the car, he would point to the wide-open fields or see cows and horses or farm equipment, that other than pictures neither one of us had ever seen before. The buildings, the houses, churches, schools—everything looked different, and then we got to this place. I've heard that bad things can happen to people out here … The farther we drove, the closer I could feel him moving toward me. I always tried to comfort him and let him know that everything would be all right, but I had no idea where we were going, and everything looked as unfamiliar to me as it did to him. Until I asked Mary the question, I just knew it had been a long ride, but not 3 hours.

Raymond wanted to know if we could spend more time together, and I told him I would try to find out what we could do for that to happen. I know at school we will be in different rooms and we can't have breakfast and lunch together, but I told him that at dinner and afterward, we would spend as much time together as we could. A big smile came over his face, and I just hoped that I was not lying to him. Every place is different, with different rules and different attitudes, and we had no idea what the unwritten rules here were going to be—not what people said the rules were, but how people act and the things they do that do not necessarily follow the rules. I've seen some workers be very nice and caring; others would cuss kids out; and even a few would hit kids. I learned it is not what people say, it is what people do, and that's what Raymond has experienced. And that is why he is nervous. In a strange place, with strange people and even though we could never go home, neither one of us had the slightest idea how to get back home even if we wanted to. We did not know what direction we were going, what roads we were on, all the turns we made, or any way of getting back even if we wanted to. We could not walk, did not see any buses, and we did not have money even if we knew how to get out of here. The only thing we could do is behave in such a way that we would stay here, or they would send us someplace else. They could send us closer or farther away from home. For now, I needed to figure this place out and do what is best for Raymond.

It was time for us to go back to our sides. I hugged Raymond and told him I would see him tomorrow. He started to cry, but I told him he had to be strong for me. I needed him to do that so I would not get in trouble. He wiped his eyes and promised not to cry. We hugged again and walked to our separate sides. He looked back at me one last time before going through the door.

1. What are some approaches to help Cori and Raymond deal with the loss of their parents?
2. Explain why you would try to place Cori and Raymond in the same adoptive home or different adoptive homes.
3. Cori shared information about her thinking that you wouldn't get from her in a therapy session. What are some techniques to work with teens who are not sharing their inner thoughts?
4. Discuss how the information you learned from Cori could be helpful when working with children in the foster care system.
5. If Cori had shared all her thoughts with you, develop a treatment plan for Cori.

# REFERENCES

Chor, K. H. B., McClelland, G. M., Weiner, D. A., Jordan, N., & Lyons, J. S. (2013). Patterns of out-of-home placement decision-making in child welfare. *Child Abuse and Neglect.* https://doi.org/10.1016/j.chiabu.2013.04.016

Crosby, S. D., Somers, C. L., Day, A. G., Zammit, M., Shier, J. M., & Baroni, B. A. (2017). Examining school attachment, social support, and trauma symptomatology among court-involved, female students. *Journal of Child and Family Studies.* https://doi.org/10.1007/s10826-017-0766-9

Den Dunnen, W., Stewart, S. L., Currie, M., Willits, E., & Baiden, P. (2013). Predictors of out-of-home placement following residential treatment. *Children and Youth Services Review.* https://doi.org/10.1016/j.childyouth.2012.12.023

Evans, R., White, J., Turley, R., Slater, T., Morgan, H., Strange, H., & Scourfield, J. (2017). Comparison of suicidal ideation, suicide attempt and suicide in children and young people in care and non-care populations: Systematic review and meta-analysis of prevalence. *Children and Youth Services Review.* https://doi.org/10.1016/j.childyouth.2017.09.020

Fratto, C. M. (2016). Trauma-informed care for youth in foster care. *Archives of Psychiatric Nursing.* https://doi.org/10.1016/j.apnu.2016.01.007

Garcia Quiroga, M., Hamilton-Giachritsis, C., & Ibañez Fanés, M. (2017). Attachment representations and socio-emotional difficulties in alternative care: A comparison between residential, foster and family based children in Chile. *Child Abuse and Neglect.* https://doi.org/10.1016/j.chiabu.2017.05.021

Gharabaghi, K., & Groskleg, R. (2010). A social pedagogy approach to residential care: Balancing education and placement in the development of an innovative child welfare residential program in Ontario, Canada. *Child Welfare.* 22(4), 19–21.

Graça, J., Calheiros, M. M., Patrício, J. N., & Magalhães, E. V. (2018). Emergency residential care settings: A model for service assessment and design. *Evaluation and Program Planning.* https://doi.org/10.1016/j.evalprogplan.2017.10.008

Horwitz, A. G., Opperman, K. J., Burnside, A., & King, C. A. (2016). Youth suicide. In *Health Promotion for Children and Adolescents.* https://doi.org/10.1007/978-1-4899-7711-3_7

James, S. (2004). Why do foster care placements disrupt? An investigation of reasons for placement change in foster care. *Social Service Review.* https://doi.org/10.1086/424546

Jansen, A. (2010). Victim or troublemaker? Young people in residential care. *Journal of Youth Studies.* https://doi.org/10.1080/13676261003801770

King, C. A., Foster, C. E., & Rogalski, K. M. (2013). *Teen suicide risk: A practitioner guide to screening, assessment, and management.* The Guilford Child and Adolescent Practitioner Series. https://doi.org/http://dx.doi.org/10.4088/JCP.14bk09608

Kroning, M., & Kroning, K. (2016). Teen depression and suicide, A SILENT CRISIS. *Journal of Christian Nursing: A Quarterly Publication of Nurses Christian Fellowship.* https://doi.org/10.1097/CNJ.0000000000000254

Lam, A., Lyons, J. S., Griffin, G., & Kisiel, C. (2015). Multiple traumatic experiences and the expression of traumatic stress symptoms for children and adolescents. *Residential Treatment for Children and Youth.* https://doi.org/10.1080/0886571X.2015.1046731

Leathers, S. J. (2006). Placement disruption and negative placement outcomes among adolescents in long-term foster care: The role of behavior problems. *Child Abuse and Neglect.* https://doi.org/10.1016/j.chiabu.2005.09.003

Leloux-Opmeer, H., Kuiper, C. H. Z., Swaab, H. T., & Scholte, E. M. (2017). Children referred to foster care, family-style group care, and residential care: (How) do they differ? *Children and Youth Services Review.* https://doi.org/10.1016/j.childyouth.2017.03.018

Little, M., Kohm, A., & Thompson, R. (2005). The impact of residential placement on child development: Research and policy implications. *International Journal of Social Welfare.* https://doi.org/10.1111/j.1468-2397.2005.00360.x

Manninen, M., Pankakoski, M., Gissler, M., & Suvisaari, J. (2015). Adolescents in a residential school for behavior disorders have an elevated mortality risk in young adulthood. *Child and Adolescent Psychiatry and Mental Health.* https://doi.org/10.1186/s13034-015-0078-z

Moreno, M. A. (2016). Preventing adolescent suicide. *JAMA Pediatrics.* https://doi.org/10.1001/jamapediatrics.2015.2561

Pirruccello, L. M. (2010). Preventing adolescent suicide: A community takes action. *Journal of Psychosocial Nursing & Mental Health Services.* https://doi.org/10.3928/02793695-20100303-01

Rodrigues, L., Calheiros, M., & Pereira, C. (2015). The decision of out-of-home placement in residential care after parental neglect: Empirically testing a psychosocial model. *Child Abuse and Neglect.* https://doi.org/10.1016/j.chiabu.2015.03.014

Salazar, A. M., Keller, T. E., Gowen, L. K., & Courtney, M. E. (2013). Trauma exposure and PTSD among older adolescents in foster care. *Social Psychiatry and Psychiatric Epidemiology.* https://doi.org/10.1007/s00127-012-0563-0

Schofield, G., Larsson, B., & Ward, E. (2017). Risk, resilience and identity construction in the life narratives of young people leaving residential care. *Child and Family Social Work.* https://doi.org/10.1111/cfs.12295

Scholte, E. M. (1997). Exploration of criteria for residential and foster care. *Journal of Child Psychology and Psychiatry and Allied Disciplines.* https://doi.org/10.1111/j.1469-7610.1997.tb01693.x

Sedlak, A. J., & Bruce, C. (2010). Youth's characteristics and backgrounds: Findings from the survey of youth in residential placement. *Juvenile Justice Bulletin.* December 2010.

Sen, R., & Broadhurst, K. (2011). Contact between children in out-of-home placements and their family and friends networks: A research review. *Child and Family Social Work*. https://doi.org/10.1111/j.1365-2206.2010.00741.x

Sim, F., Li, D., & Chu, C. M. (2016). The moderating effect between strengths and placement on children's needs in out-of-home care: A follow-up study. *Children and Youth Services Review*. https://doi.org/10.1016/j.childyouth.2015.11.012

Ward, A. (2004). Towards a theory of the everyday: The ordinary and the special in daily living in residential care. *Child and Youth Care Forum*. https://doi.org/10.1023/B:CCAR.0000029686.10310.49

# CHAPTER 5

# A College Experience

*Jessica Campbell*

## INTRODUCTION

When did you know you were going to college? Was there a milestone moment, or as far back as you can remember, that was your destination? Since most people don't have a college degree, there must have been some awareness, discussion, or tradition that resulted in you taking that step. For most people, including children in foster care, college is not an option. This case study will discuss a teenager who aged out of the foster care system and against several challenges enrolled in college. We will also learn about a college program that provides services and supports to help students transition from child welfare to college graduate. For this case study, the program will be called Fostering Laker Success.

## BARRIERS TO FOSTER CHILDREN ATTENDING COLLEGE

The creation of college-based child welfare support programs is to help youth who have experienced foster care to see a path to college. Using the state of Michigan as an example, according to the Michigan Education Trust, 70% of teens emancipated from foster care report that they want to attend college, but fewer than 10% who graduate from high school enroll in college, and of those less than 1% graduate from college. Approximately 13,000 children are in the Michigan foster care system at any given time. A growing number of Michigan youth are reaching adult age while in foster care and have no clear path to attend college after high school.

Many teenagers are not academically or financially able to attend college. Others never had a conversation about it, believe they are not smart enough, or, in their environment, people don't go to college. There can be challenges in the foster home, challenges with the biological family, challenges at school, and challenges building relationships with other children that influence decisions into adulthood. This college vision of the future is not part of their dinner table conversation. Sometimes caseworkers and other professionals don't help children set college as a goal. Caseworkers are trying to protect the children from continued abuse or neglect, addressing the trauma that the children have experienced and trying to find a permanent placement for the children, which could include returning to biological parents, relatives, remaining in foster care, or adoption.

Additionally, caseworkers have high caseloads and lots of paperwork, and they must prioritize what areas they can address. Because a significant number of children are struggling in school due to the issues impacting their lives, the goal could be trying to address the trauma, create stability, and get them to graduate from high school with the independent living skills to live on their own, as opposed to focusing on applying for college.

The John H. Chafee Foster Care Independent Living Act of 1999 (CFCIP) offers assistance to help current and former foster care students achieve self-sufficiency. States and Native American nations can receive grants by submitting a plan to assist in a wide variety of areas designed to support a successful transition to adulthood. Activities and programs include, but are not limited to, help with education, employment, financial management, housing, emotional support, and assured connections to caring adults. The program serves those likely to remain in foster care until age 18; youth who, after attaining 16 years of age, have left foster care for kinship guardianship or adoption; and young adults ages 18–21 who have aged out of the foster care system.

The Education and Training Vouchers (ETV) program was added to the John H. Chafee Foster Care Independence Program, under the U.S. Department of Health and Human Services in 2002 for youths aging out of foster care. ETV provides resources specifically to meet the educational and training needs of youth in addition to the existing authorization for the CFCIP program. The law authorizes payments to states and Native American nations through postsecondary education and training vouchers for youth likely to experience difficulty as a transition to adulthood after the age of 18. The program makes available yearly vouchers for postsecondary education and training for eligible youth.

### QUESTIONS

All these questions relate to your home state.

1. What is the current number of children in the foster care system?
2. What is the average percentage of children who aged out of the foster care system over the last five years?
3. Over the last five years, what is the percentage of foster children who graduate from high school?

4. Over the last five years, what is the percentage of foster children who attended college?
5. Of those who attended college, what percentage graduated from college?
6. In the general population of your state, what is the percentage of people with a college degree?

---

## WHAT IS FOSTERING LAKER SUCCESS?

The Fostering Laker Success program is a federal Department of State grant brought to the university to address the needs of youth in college who come from foster care or other out-of-home placements. The grant allowed for the hiring of a campus life coach to focus on this population. Each student must be approved by the federal Department of State, under the age of 23, eligible for Youth in Transition funding, and have been in qualified foster care or non-secure delinquency placement supervised by the State Department at age 14 or older. Eligible placements include licensed foster family homes, relatives' homes, group homes, emergency shelters, childcare institutions for fewer than 25 children, independent living, and semi-independent living placements.

The goal of Fostering Laker Success is to increase access and success in higher education and post-college careers. Fostering Laker Success uses a holistic approach in addressing the following areas:

- maintaining healthy relationships
- work and study habits
- planning and goal setting
- using community resources
- daily living activities
- budgeting and paying bills
- computer literacy
- permanent connections to caring adults

## MEET THE LIFE COACH

The university hired me to implement the Fostering Laker Success program and to be the life coach. My role as life coach is to help students navigate college, access funding resources, and develop life skills such as proactive problem solving, time management, organization of self and others, healthy eating habits, managing health and hygiene, and much more.

I began at the start of the fall academic year, working with the Dean of Students' office to develop a list of students who met the eligibility requirements for Fostering Laker Success. I met with our support services departments, counseling center, academic units, student organizations, and faculty governance to talk about Fostering Laker Success, explain the mission and goals of the program, and for their assistance in referring students to the program. I worked with the marketing department to share information in the university's social media while being careful not to identify the students in a negative light, but rather as a support network for those students who were interested in or were unaware of the services that we could provide at the university. I also contacted local, regional, and state child welfare agencies, programs, and advocacy groups to make them aware of the Fostering Laker Success program. I hoped that people would be more likely to talk to children in foster care about college if they were aware of the services and supports in place.

Once I had the program set up, the next step was reaching out to students while being respectful of student confidentiality. The initial contact was by individual email sent to students to explain the program and the opportunities that it afforded. I know that some people identify themselves as foster children, while others try to move beyond that label or are embarrassed by that label. Therefore, if students wanted to participate in Fostering Laker Success, I provided multiple venues and multiple opportunities where students could participate at their level of comfort.

## MEETING KARA

A month into the fall semester of her second year in college, Kara reconnected with the counselor in the university counseling center. She met with the counselor weekly for 30 minutes and attended Alcoholics Anonymous (AA) several times a week. Her counselor mentioned Fostering Laker Success to Kara. Her initial reaction was, "I don't need another person trying to control me. I have a lot of appointments already. I don't want anyone else in my business."

After explaining more about the program and the connection to other students who lived in foster care, Kara appeared interested in learning more about the program and talking to other students in foster care.

One day a referral came from the counselor. The counselor had talked with Kara about the Fostering Laker Success program, and Kara agreed to the counselor making a referral and providing some background information. While Kara agreed to the referral, the counselor felt that Kara would not contact me on her own and that I would need to reach out to her, probably on several occasions, before Kara would meet with me.

I sent several emails over a few weeks to Kara with no response. Then one day, I received an email from Kara asking to meet with me. However, when it came time for the appointment, she did not show up. I emailed her about the missed appointment and asked her to reschedule. Kara did, and once again did not show. Eventually, Kara stopped responding to my emails. However, she still received emails about the program and a schedule of activities. One of those activities was a community dinner for university students who have been in foster care or other out-of-home placements. From the referral, Kara had always wanted to meet other students with similar experiences. Kara attended the dinner, and we met for the first time. She also met students who understood living in foster care. Feeling a connection, she decided to meet with me.

The next day Kara received an email from me to schedule a one-on-one meeting. Again, she scheduled a meeting, but this time she kept the appointment.

I greeted her with a smile and a handshake. She touched my hand and quickly pulled away. Moving into my office, Kara looked nervous, making little eye contact as she looked around the office. Along with my desk, there are two large chairs and an end table. I asked her to sit and pointed to the chairs. I never pick a chair but let them decide where they want to sit. I introduced myself again and briefly explained my role at the university.

> "Thank you for coming. How are you doing today?" I asked.
> "Good."
> "Thanks for coming to the dinner. I hope you had a good time?"
> "It was nice. The food was good."
> "You are welcome to come to any of our events. We are happy to have you there."

I told her about Fostering Laker Success, the event she attended, and gave some examples of our student support programs. I asked if she had any questions, but she said no.

> "How did your first year at the university go?"
> "I passed all my classes."
> "Congratulations. How does it feel to be one year closer to being a college graduate?"

Kara look surprised by my comment. Many students only focus on one semester at a time; the end seems so far away, and they think about all the things that can go wrong. I like placing a positive image in their mind regarding the outcome: graduation.

> "Have you decided on a major?"
> "I keep changing my mind."

"Most students change majors when they get to college. They find out about new fields and career paths. You have more choices than you probably thought you had when you started."

"This is my second year of college, and everyone around me seems to know what they want to do, but me."

"Instead of selecting a major, what are some areas you are interested in?"

She hesitated before answering. "I don't know yet. I have a number of ideas, but I haven't decided which way to go. People think I should do something in the helping profession because of my background and experiences."

"Is that a possibility?" I asked.

"Not for me. The only helping profession I know moved me out of my home, separated me from my siblings, moved me from house to house, and at the age of 18 said, 'You're grown and on your own now.' That does not sound much like a helping profession to me. Why would I want to do that to some other kid?"

When I said, "What you describe doesn't sound much like a helping profession to me," I saw a slightly surprised look on her face, and a little tension left the room.

I kept my questions general, gave her opportunities to talk, and shared a little about myself, so it would not feel like all the attention was on her. This approach helped Kara talk more about herself. In the meeting, I focused on the direction she wanted to go. I know that students are trying to figure out their place in the world. Most of their lives, the adults around them have made the decisions for them. If it is a foster care worker, therapist, attorney, judge, or any professional in their life, those people impact their outcome.

The students I meet with don't know who I am or what power I have over their lives. What they know is I am running a program for students like them. I am at a large, complicated university, and I am in a position of power, but they don't know to what degree. They could wonder if I can see their grades, talk to their professors, or even decide if they stay at the university. While the answer to those and other questions is no, that is not their frame of reference. The key is, I approach the relationship from how *they* might see me, not what my role truly is. Over time they will come to understand my role, which some will accept, and others will always be suspicious of to protect themselves.

Kara said, "I enjoy art and music. My science and political science classes were interesting. I felt like I learned something, and grade-wise, I did well in those classes."

This opened a line of communication where I felt Kara becoming more comfortable with me. I shared more information about Fostering Laker Success and explained how we could develop a program based on her needs.

We talked until it was time for her to go to class. She wanted to meet again in a couple of days to get help with some of the services we provide.

## NEXT MEETING

At the next meeting with Kara, she appeared agitated, breathing quickly, moving in her chair, and seemed unfocused. I asked how she was doing. At first, she sat there quietly, looking into the distance. Her breathing became shallow. Her eyes moved to look at me, and Kara started crying. I handed her some tissues and gave her time to compose herself.

"It's hard, you know. I have so much going on, and I need help. I want to stop drinking and using drugs. I want to do better in school. It's hard, and no one understands that. I am trying my best … but … I can't. I just can't. I don't want to do this anymore!" Kara kept crying.

Once again, I provided time for Kara to self-soothe before asking my next question. "What do you mean you don't want to do this anymore?"

"(Rolling her eyes) I am not going to kill myself! Things are just hard."
"Thanks for the clarification. How can I best support you?"
"I don't know. I thought that was your job?"
"Okay, well, let's start with prioritizing."
"Sure."

Every student is different when it comes to what they need to be successful in school and life. Fostering Laker Success focuses on life needs, which are mostly basic needs that will help with school.

I create a checklist tailored to the individual. They can include doctors' appointments, food, clothes, counseling, medical insurance card, credit report, financial aid documents, tribal card, birth certificate, state ID/driver's license, social security card, housing, winter apparel, backpacks, bedding, school supplies, proof of registration, etc.

Kara has issues with substances, isolation, wanting to connect with family, succeeding in college, getting an education, support from family, and questioning some of the values and beliefs in her family. She struggles with whether she is going to be like her family and why it is wrong to want to be like them. Some students' college and related experiences can make them feel like they are selling out or forgetting where they came from. People want to connect to family, friends, and community. When they don't have that connection, they try to find it, or feel lost, and some are depressed because something is missing.

We can't replace those things, but we can help create an environment that provides some support, comfort, and security. We know that students are not as successful if they feel isolated. Take that and add growing up without a sense of belonging, and college can feel like a large, isolating place where you don't fit in or are not sure how to fit in. Some feel other students are smarter and had advantages they did not have and wonder if they even belong in college.

They bring to college the issues they dealt with in foster care—poor relationships, mental health, abuse, and rejection. They are also learning new systems, about being an adult, having more responsibilities, and being held accountable for their actions.

## BASIC NEEDS

I quickly discovered that many of Kara's basic needs had not been met. During the first few sessions, I worked with Kara on getting an insurance card, accessing health care resources, and addressing food needs. We talked to the insurance agency to get her insurance card and provided resources that accepted their insurance. We spoke of the on-campus health center that offers a wide variety of resources. Together, we made an appointment.

Additionally, we worked together to get access to previous medical documents and identification information. Helping Kara with these tasks built trust. Kara finally felt like there was positive movement in her life. I would focus another time on the fact that she went through foster care and was in her second year of college. Because of her determination, there was already positive movement in her life.

Through Fostering Laker Success, Kara received a mentor, allowing her to have another supportive adult at the university. At first, she did not engage with the mentor, but over time became more active. Her mentor, Lindsey, introduced Kara to Shakespeare and many other plays on campus. Later, Kara learned she had a love for theater. Kara shared with her mentor that she loved art and was considering getting back into drawing. Her mentor purchased her art supplies, and Kara returned the favor by make a beautiful piece of art for her mentor. (Later, Kara signed up for art classes at the university and is now considering changing her major to art.) Lindsey also aided Kara in expanding her campus network by introducing her to other campus professionals with whom Kara may interact throughout her time here at the university. Kara mentioned to me in one of our coaching sessions:

> "I like my mentor, but we are always doing something."
> "What do you mean?"
> "She is always taking me places and introducing me to people across campus. I feel like it's another class."

"That sounds like a good thing …?"

"It kinda is but, I don't know."

"Okay?"

"Well, I do enjoy meeting new people and going to plays but, I feel weird … like why is she doing all this? I don't know, it's weird."

I said, "She volunteered to be a mentor for the program. She enjoys spending her time helping others. She knows that having a mentor can dramatically improve outcomes for students."

"That makes sense; I thought she felt bad for me."

"No, she just likes working to help students succeed."

"That's cool. We are going to the museum later this week. I think I will make another art piece for her."

"That's very nice of you, but you know you don't have to."

"I know, I want to. She is nice, and I like hanging out with her. Plus, she gives me good feedback."

Kara continued to meet with me and became more open with her status of sobriety and desire to be clean. I worked with Kara to develop processes to stop drinking. Not many of them were successful, but while Kara never felt I judged or was disappointed in her, she wanted me to see she was trying and did not want me to be disappointed with her. She felt she had someone by her side fighting this fight with her. Kara attended the community dinners to connect with other students, financial aid presentations to help students understand their financial aid packages, and other programming events that would help her be successful at the university.

## QUESTIONS

1. Why do you think Kara came back to meet with her coach?
2. Update your social assessment of Kara based on the additional information.
3. Identify Kara's strengths.
4. List areas to work on with Kara, and rank them.
5. Explain the reason for the item you ranked number one.

## HOME LIFE

Students bring their life experiences to college. Sometimes they share them, keep to themselves, or are unaware that those experiences influence decisions, demeanor, and relationships.

From the information Kara shared and my conversations with the counselor, I had a brief history of Kara's time in foster care. Kara was placed in foster care at the age of 11 and aged out of the system at 18 years old. Kara grew up in a small town in Michigan. Many of the people in Kara's town suffered from alcoholism and drug abuse, including her mother. Her father fell victim to addiction and left the family. Kara does not remember how old she was when he left. He left several times, but the last time he did not come back. Often, Kara and her younger siblings (Matthew, 9, and Janet, 8, at the time) would be left with a babysitter for days. However, when no sitter was available, they were left alone. Kara became a surrogate parent for her siblings. She tried to take care of the house and provide for her siblings, the best a child could. She recalls her focus at the time was protecting her younger siblings from feeling the loss of absent parents. That was the way for as long as she could remember. That led to chronic absences from school, which is how Child Protective Services (CPS) first got involved. Schools are mandated to report truant students.

CPS conducted its first investigation when Kara was 11. They discovered that the mother was not able to provide for her children, and Kara and her siblings entered the foster care system. During her time in foster care, she lived in three different homes: with her grandparents, who had their son (Kara's uncle) living with them; with family friends Teresa and John Smith; and her aunt and uncle, Jackie and Mike.

Over the next month, Kara attended one of our dinners, and we had two more coaching sessions. It was during our sessions that Kara talked more about her family and her time in foster care.

## KARA IN FOSTER CARE

Through our continuous coaching sessions, I was able to get a better understanding of Kara's environment before college.

The first foster home for Kara and her siblings was with their grandparents. Financially, the grandparents were doing very well and in good health. Kara returned to the same school and began improving academically. However, she was having trouble adjusting to her new environment. She followed the rules and did what she could, but she had difficulty falling asleep at night, focusing on extracurricular activities, and felt distant from friends. It was a little under two years when her grandparents informed Kara and her siblings that it was time for them to live somewhere else. Kara was shocked and hurt. Once again, her voice and demeanor said her family failed to be there for her.

"The most frustrating part is that they never told me why."

Kara said the same day they told them they were moving, their caseworker showed up to help them pack and told them about the new placement.

"What shocked us even more than moving was they were not going to place us together. I started yelling at the worker and saw Matthew and Janet crying. Seeing how upset they were, I stopped yelling so I could put my arms around them. I was also crying," said Kara.

It had been several years since this happened, but I could see the emotions coming to the surface. I was not sure if I should change the subject or let Kara continue. I decided to let Kara talk about whatever she wanted because it was clear it was having an impact on her well-being and education. Moreover, Fostering Laker Success was here to help in those areas.

Kara said the new foster parents were family friends, Teresa and John. They had two children of their own (Jacob, 10, and Mike, 11). Matthew and Janet were placed with another family because John and Teresa only had room for one of them.

"I did not like being separated from Matthew and Janet," said Kara. "I did not know where they were going, who the people were, or when I would see them again."

With the move, she also changed schools. Not knowing anyone at the school, Kara stayed to herself. At home, she was forced to clean up the house and care for the younger children. Cleaning and caring for the children was not an issue for her because she was used to it. Knowing no one in the neighborhood, Kara had a lot of free time and found her grades improving at school.

But her desire to go home and be with her mother and siblings was still present. Her mother was not following the treatment plan, which prevented visitation at that time. Kara attended therapy but never felt like talking about what happened. From her point of view, talking was what got her into this mess.

"How long was it before you saw your brother and sister?"

"It was a month before I saw them. The caseworker said that because they were younger, they needed more time to adjust to the new home. I told her I could help them adjust, but she would not listen to me."

"Did you tell the caseworker about all the work you were doing around the house?"

"No one was listening to anything I had to say. I knew how to take care of myself if caseworkers would let me. And I knew how to help Matthew and Janet, but everyone knew more than me. I did not tell the caseworker about the work in the home because why would she believe me. And if she did, I would have gotten moved to another home that could have been worse," said Kara. "I could have run away, but I knew I would not see Matthew and Janet if I did. So I stayed."

"How long did you live with them?"

"I lived there for three years."

Kara recalls that after three years, a new caseworker showed up to relocate her to another home. Once again, Kara packed up what she had and headed to another placement. Through all this, Kara blamed herself. She couldn't understand what she was doing wrong, and how come no one wanted her? She did what they asked and then some. At this point, Kara was 16 years old.

## QUESTIONS

1. Kara is out of the foster care system, so you don't have access to her child welfare file. Based on the information provided by Kara, what questions do you have about her time in foster care?

2. Most people who work in foster care would say that the way Kara described her moves would not happen that way. Assuming they are correct, discuss why you think Kara described her foster care experience the way she did.

3. Based on further investigation, we found out the way Kara explained her placements was correct. Discuss a few ways you would have handled it differently, and why.

## HER FINAL PLACEMENT

When Kara discovered her next placement was with her aunt Jackie and uncle Mike, she was excited. They were fun people she enjoyed being around. Kara hoped that Matthew and Janet could join her at Aunt Jackie's house, but the foster care worker told her that they were in a stable home, and she did not want to move them. The worker said she would increase the number of visits. While Kara was disappointed about not being with her brother and sister, she was happy to be staying with family. She also thought she would get to spend time with her mother.

Kara described the first couple of months as "awesome." She learned more about her extended family, what her mother was like as a child, and attended community events together. During the summer, Kara figured she would get a job so she could have some extra money and not burden her aunt and uncle. Kara was able to find a job in the community but needed transportation. Jackie and Mike refused to take her back and forth to work. They told her it wasn't what they signed up for. Every day, Kara had to search for a ride to and from work.

When it was time to go back to school, Jackie and Mike told Kara they would pay for what she needed to start school, but after that, she would need to use her work money to buy her supplies and clothes. They told her to ask the foster care worker if she needed anything else. The state has plenty of money, and Jackie and Mike were not going to spend all their money on her. Kara informed her caseworker of what was going on, and she told her there was not much she could do. This behavior continued throughout her time in the home.

After a year with Aunt Jackie and Uncle Mike, the caseworker told Kara that she and her siblings would return to their mother. Kara was 17 years old. Kara was happy her family would be together again, and she could take care of her younger siblings. She felt overwhelmed to have her family together. However, it took less than a month at home to notice that her mother was not only drinking again but also using drugs. Kara returned to the very same situation she left: she and her two siblings were just older.

"My mom had a job, but still drank and did drugs. I guess she did less of it than before we left," Kara said. "My mother did a good job of covering up the drinking and drugs, and I never told anyone because I was home with Matthew and Janet, and if I said anything, they would move us again."

---

**QUESTION**

1. Based on the information you have, why do you think Kara and her siblings moved three times, and why was she separated from her siblings?

---

## KARA'S SECOND YEAR OF COLLEGE

At the start of the fall semester, Kara came back to campus as early as she could. She got her books and school supplies and was ready for the first week of classes. Within the first week of class, her friends threw a party, complete with drugs and alcohol. Initially, she was not going to go, but one of her friends did not want to go alone. And other friends of hers texted and continually called. She went to the party with another friend who was also working on staying sober. Neither of them achieved that goal. It was 30 minutes into the party before they both had a drink in their hand. Kara did not take any drugs that night but did get extremely drunk.

In the next few days, she was extremely disappointed in herself. Feeling that she was on the same path as her mother, she had an anxiety attack. She missed classes for the next couple of days. Upon checking her email, Kara saw something about Fostering Laker Success. She quickly dismissed it and went on with her day. She went to class the following week and attempted to catch up with her work and get back on track. It wasn't long before there was another college party, in which she attended and had some drinks (but didn't get blackout-drunk). The next day her emotions were at an all-time high. She swore not to go out again that semester.

## KARA'S THIRD YEAR OF COLLEGE WITH FOSTERING LAKER SUCCESS

At the end of her second year, Kara went home for the summer (her mother's house). She saw both her siblings working jobs, only to spend their nights partying and drinking heavily (neither of whom was old enough to drink). She saw her past friends from high school pregnant, using drugs, and living at home with no future. At that moment, Kara knew she needed to finish college. There was no other way.

"I spent the summer in my room, avoiding my family and friends," she said.

After taking the summer off to rest and get ready, she returned for her third year. She was armed with a living skills coach, mentor, counselor, and a new friend group. She turned down party invitations and focused on her schoolwork.

One night she got a call from her siblings complaining about their mother. Kara felt she was getting sucked back into her past, which she desperately tried to escape. Kara and I met, and she expressed her frustrations with her family. We talked about the locus of control. Over the next few sessions, Kara and I processed her family relationships and how they impacted her. Kara was able to understand that she could not change her siblings or her mother. Through this, Kara also became open to the idea of seeking counseling outside of the university so that she could have weekly hour-long sessions.

Kara still occasionally drinks but does not get blackout-drunk and is entirely off drugs. Kara has a plan for her future and understands it is an uphill battle but believes with the support she receives from Fostering Laker Success, she will be a success.

"I feel like I have hope."

"That is awesome."

"Yeah, I want to do something, help people, and graduate."

"That sounds like a great plan."

"I feel like I am learning what things I can do stuff about. I know my mother will not be the mother I want her to be, and that hurts."

"Yes, that is understandable, and it is okay to feel that way."

"Really ... thank you. I just want to be successful and graduate."

"You are already making great strides. You meet with me regularly, you connect with your mentor, you have signed up for tutoring, regularly going to counseling, and you are motivated and ready to continue the change."

"Yeah, Yeah, I am."

1. What challenges does Kara continue to face?
2. What services would you like to see Fostering Laker Success provide for Kara?
3. How do you see Kara's future based on your assessment?
4. If Kara tells you her mother is not taking care of her siblings, what is your legal responsibility, if any?
5. What is the role of confidentiality in what Kara has told you?

## REFERENCES

Greer, R. D. (2016). A critical reflection: Foster care youth experiences at a four year postsecondary institution (Order No. 10138153). *Available from Social Science Premium Collection* (1803589342). Retrieved from http://search.proquest.com. ezproxy.gvsu.edu/docview/1803589342?accountid=39473

Gillum, N. L., Durrant, L., Mendez-Grant, M., Wells, P., & Jaber, A. (2018). College students' beliefs about a campus support program for college students who experienced foster care. *College Student Affairs Journal, 36*(1), 32.

Huang, H., Fernandez, S., Rhoden, M., & Joseph, R. (2018). Serving former foster youth and homeless students in college. *Journal of Social Service Research, 44*(2), 209–222.

Geiger, J. M., Cheung, J. R., Hanrahan, J. E., Lietz, C. A., & Carpenter, B. M. (2017). Increasing competency, self-confidence, and connectedness among foster care alumni entering a 4-year university: Findings from an early-start program. *Journal of Social Service Research, 43*(5), 566–579.

John H. Chafee Foster Care Independent Living Act of 1999. https://www.acf.hhs. gov/cb/resource/chafee-foster-care-program

Kinarsky, A. R. (2017). Fostering success: Understanding the experience of foster youth undergraduates. *Children & Youth Services Review, 81,* 220–228.

Michigan Education Trust. (2018). https://www.michigan.gov/setwithmet/

Michigan Educational Training Voucher. (2018). https://mietv.samaritas.org/

Okpych, N. (2012). Policy framework supporting youth aging-out of foster care through college: Review and recommendations. *Children and Youth Services Review, 34*(7), 1390–1396.

Rios, S. J., & Rocco, T. S. (2014). From foster care to college: Barriers and supports on the road to postsecondary education. *Emerging Adulthood, 2*(3), 227–237.

Salazar, A. M. (2012). Supporting college success in foster care alumni: Salient factors related to postsecondary retention. *Child Welfare, 91*(5), 139–167.

Salazar, A. M., Jones, K. R., Emerson, J. C., & Mucha, L. (2016). Postsecondary strengths, challenges, and supports experienced by foster care alumni college graduates. *Journal of College Student Development, 57*(3), 263–279.

Schelbe, L., Day, A., Geiger, J. M., & Piel, M. H. (2019). The state of evaluations of campus-based support programs serving foster care alumni in higher education. *Child Welfare, 97*(2), 23–40.

# CHAPTER 6

# Best Practices

*George Grant, Jr.*

## INTRODUCTION

Working on the cases in this book can make you a little uncomfortable by exposing you to situations most people have never seen, find it difficult to imagine, and not part of their worldview. Therefore, because these cases can be overwhelming and stressful, it is necessary to have a foundation of best practices to assist you and your clients.

Best practices are agreed-upon practices, approaches, and research that address effective ways to achieve the desired outcome. Each field of practice has its own best practices. Some are unique to that field, while others overlap with other fields. There is conflict and debate over best practices, and they can evolve. As new information emerges, we wonder why professionals thought what they were doing was correct. Let us give you a couple of examples.

There were practices that forbade foster parents to adopt the children placed in their home. With the plan for the reunification of the children with their biological parents, child welfare agencies did not want the foster family becoming too attached to the children, making it difficult to remove the children from the foster parents. The prevailing wisdom was that the children would bond with the foster family, and with the improved living conditions would prefer to remain with the foster family rather than returning to their biological home. You can see the reasoning behind this thinking and why this would have been considered best practice. They were trying to address the emotional needs of the children and foster families.

Today, the best practice is wanting the foster parents to adopt the children if they become eligible for adoption. The term *fost-adopt* or *foster-adopt* means foster care-to-adoption, when the foster family is told about the possibility of adoption if parental rights are terminated and the court states the child is eligible for adoption. With more intentionality, this can reduce the number of placements children face, and if there is a strong emotional bond with the foster family, it will result in a successful, permanent (a forever home) placement.

One additional example from the past is the use of orphanages in the care of children. The impetus of orphanages was the protection of children who were abused, neglected, or abandoned. There was a large number of children who needed someplace to stay. This was seen as a best practice in that it met the needs of children with no other supports.

Over time, it became clear that some orphanages treated children no better than the environment from which they were protecting them. Growing up in an orphanage brought no sense of family, a loss of culture, and without a sense of how to function as adults. A lot of children were placed in orphanages because they came from low-income homes headed by female single parents. Poverty emerged as the reason most children were in orphanages. Therefore, the best practice of orphanages gradually changed to foster homes becoming the best practice.

There are many topics like state government versus federal government in the protection of children; do children experience trauma; should children be placed with relatives; grandparents' rights; and the thousands of laws, policies, and practices that have changed, evolved, and disappeared over time. Each area would have been considered best practices at one time. Not that everyone agreed with those practices at the time, but if they were considered acceptable by leaders in the field, lawmakers, practitioners, and academics, they could be called best practices.

However, best practices can have no data-driven approach to show those approaches work or were in the clients' best interests. A policy, law, or practice had to be based—and continues to be based—on personal beliefs and the power to carry out those beliefs. If you believe that poor people are lazy, your best practice will reflect that belief. What do you think about public schools, private schools, welfare benefits, single parents, substance abuse, L.G.B.T.Q.I.A.+. rights, religion, and homelessness? You may not have the power to make them best practices, but you could make them best practices with your clients. If your belief is poor people are lazy and you want to work with them because you know how to stop them from being lazy, there may be no evidence around that belief other than your personal conviction. You have turned something you believe about your clients into your best practices.

The idea behind best practices should be using methods, theories, and approaches when working with clients and systems that have shown to help achieve the desired client-focused goals or outcomes. A few examples are what is the best way to talk to a child who has been abused; what techniques have been successful when working with teens with a substance abuse addiction; or how best to work with a person experiencing domestic violence. From the research, literature, and practice, we want to learn what produces positive client outcomes.

Another way to understand best practices is to start from an internal perspective. Our position is that best practices do not start with the client; rather, it is through self-reflection. Therefore, this chapter will discuss best practices from an internal view moving outward to the clients and systems you are interacting with related to the cases you have reviewed.

## SELF-CARE

This section will focus on several best practices that will provide some depth regarding your role and responsibilities and the systems you interact with. One of the hardest things for people to do is self-care.

1. Why did you select this field? Not what you want to do—e.g., save children or fight for the poor—you could do that with any degree or even without a degree.

There is a lot of information that addresses ethical behaviors when interacting with clients and systems. In any job, relationship, and environment, what guides you is your beliefs. A better way to say it is how you look and feel about yourself. From our physical appearance, socioeconomic class, education, and mental, emotional, family, and life experiences, we are all different.

Therefore, best practices are concepts and theories that produce different outcomes based on the factors that determine how the person sees themselves. However, turn that around, and it is the factors that determine how you see yourself.

### Robert's First Job

Just graduating from college, it was my first day on the job as a foster care worker. I was excited and nervous about putting into practice all the things that I had learned. Meeting new people, how to remember everyone's name, and just making my way around the building made me anxious and exhilarated. I worried about my caseload and not wanting to mess up.

My focus was not on self-care. And while I learned about self-care in class and in my internship, I was young and not worried about myself; I wanted to do what I got the degree to do, help people. Up early and late to bed was nothing to me. What I did in college, I was successful in my classes, and I graduated. So, I did not see the need to do anything differently from what I had been doing.

It was my supervisor who talked about the job, the caseload, where things were in the building, and took me around to meet my peers. Name after name was flying by, and I knew it was going to be a while before I could put names and faces together. That was the anxiety I was feeling in this new position.

After a couple of days of getting situated in the job, understanding the paperwork requirements, and whom to go to when I had a question, next came talking about cases. I would review several cases and write assessments and develop intervention plans. Once I got feedback, I would shadow my supervisor on a couple of his cases. He said within the next couple of weeks as new cases came, they would be assigned to me, unless there was some reason that it was in the best interest of the client to assign them to someone else.

After a few days, my supervisor came to my office to talk about my adjustment and how I was feeling. His next topic dealt with self-care. He talked about issues of stress, taking the job home, seeing things I had only read about, and seeing abuse and neglect everywhere I went. He told me that everyone takes their cases home in the beginning. The key is doing everything you could do that day, believing it, and being able to leave the cases at work. If you're constantly thinking about what you did, what you could have done, and did you make the situation better or worse, it will only cause stress. You're going to think about information or an idea that you should have shared with the client, but you didn't think about it at the time. He talked about the questions to ask myself, ways to think about my role, and how that information can help me be successful in the job or learn that this is not the right job for me.

I was taken aback by this not being the right job for me because I just started this job. I knew in college this was what I wanted to do, and now here I am working in the field I wanted to work in. There is no way this could not be the right job. Once I got over my panic attack, my supervisor showed me I was doing the very thing that he was talking about. Internalizing what he was saying was like taking the job home. I was processing every word, every comment, everything he said, and I was applying it to how it related to me. But I wasn't applying it from a self-care point of view. Instead, I was looking at it from why people would think this is not the right job for me, or people thinking I can't do a good job. I was placing stress on myself, which, once I got my caseload, would take time, energy, and perspective away from the client because I was too busy worrying about what people thought about me. It had been less than a week, but it was an extremely powerful lesson that would help me in my career.

### QUESTIONS

Try answering some of these questions. Reflect on your answers as part of your self-care.

1. Why are you in this field?
2. What do you think about the clients who receive your services?
3. What are your goals?
4. What do you want out of this job?

With your family and friends, you are not a social worker, counselor, therapist, or caseworker, you are a family member or friend—so act like one. You have the skills you learned, and sometimes there is a tendency to put them in play in nonwork situations. You may also have family members and friends who see you as the person they can come to with their problems because of your training and education. Be careful not to fall into the trap of being something different from your role as a family member or friend. You may have information or advice that you can give, and that's fine to do. But don't turn those interactions into therapy sessions.

Have friends outside of your profession so you don't spend all your time outside of work talking about work. Your interests can be wide and varied, and those outside your profession can challenge you to think differently and engage in activities that differ from those at work.

Find a mentor or mentors you can trust to give you advice and direction and act as a sounding board. Mentors can help you adjust to your job, develop ways to find breaks and separation, and can give you honest feedback and direction. You are not looking for people who will agree with you all the time or disagree with you all the time. You're looking for mentors who will give honest feedback.

## Self-Care Continued

Dealing with difficult cases, you must learn to take care of yourself. Learn self-care by managing how you eat, sleep, exercise, and vacation. Learn to care for yourself in order to help your clients. Learn to separate work from personal life. Do all you can at work, and when you go home, leave work at work. Know your field. Know other fields. Learn laws, policies, potential changes, and how they impacted your clients and your ability to do your job. Know your code of ethics. Acknowledge your power. You have more power than your clients. Learn about programs and techniques others are using. Ideas and approaches can come from other people. Not every idea and everything published is the right idea for your clients. Keep growing in your field.

Learn to work with systems that impact your job, including court systems, elected officials, community groups, and funders. Understanding diversity, equity, and inclusion, and the role they play on your clients and how you manage your job. Learn to build relationships that can give you access to people and information that could help your clients. Understand what you can control and what you can't control. List individuals and organizations that set policies and laws that influence how you do your work. Continue to learn and expand your therapy approaches.

Things to think about include: How do clients see/view themselves? How do they see the systems with which they must interact? How do the systems see your clients?

Become a lifelong learner by using training, conferences, online programs, and discussion groups. Bring joy to your job instead of trying to find joy *at* the job. Enjoy what you do and remember you are making a difference in the lives of others.

Learn to take care of your financial resources. Understand your benefits, take advantage of the resources and supports your employer provides, learn about investing, and learn to make your own informed financial decisions.

## The Stress

The stress of working in child welfare affects everyone differently. Some people can spend their careers in the field and love what they do, while others change fields or change interests. Some burn out or leave before they burn out. Others get into the field for a job but are not in the right field. Finally, people have a difficult time managing their resources and cannot afford to leave a job for which they have no passion.

# POWER

Do you see yourself as having power or not having power? Clients see you as having power. How do you see yourself, and how do your clients see you? Understanding the client is the expert in their world and how they live and survive in that world. You may think to yourself, I could never live like that. But your focus is not how you would live but how the client is living.

The starting point for best practices starts with you. You know the case better than anyone. Unless your reputation is damaged, most people will believe what you say. That is power. You, and only you, will decide how that power is used.

## Mary Has Power

I have been working in a human service agency for a little over ten years. I started in direct service and over time moved into administration. Now I supervise 25 people in our adult services program. The issue and role of power has always been a discussion point for people. Over my time interacting with people in my organization and in other organizations, that concept of power always comes up.

I would hear people say that they didn't understand why their client was upset with them because they don't make the rules; they just enforce them. They would say there are times they didn't agree with the rules, but since they didn't have any power, all they could do was implement the rules as told to them. I would also hear them say it was their supervisor, executive director, state legislators, governor, the state department of human service who have power, and if clients were upset, go see them.

What I find fascinating is there are always degrees of power. The people who are wealthier than others, people who have more influence, people who just by a cult of personality have more people following them than others. So, the issue of power will always exist. But within those degrees, we all have some power.

When a worker would say, "I don't have any power," my reaction was "You have more power than the clients you serve. You're not going to them for assistance or help; they are coming to you. There is some circumstance that has resulted in them coming to you for assistance to resolve the issues that they are dealing with. That means you have power, and you have more power than the people who are coming to see you. So, I believe that makes your position of lack of power weak."

I would hear people ask, "Why are clients coming to me about a policy issue? I didn't make the policy, they should go to the state legislators to get that changed." But when I asked that person, "As an advocate for the client, why haven't you gone to the state legislators to get that policy changed?" the response was "I don't have access to legislators to make that happen." My response was "With your experience, education, and understanding of policy and resources, if you don't have access to the policy makers, how would your clients have access to them?" I never got a good answer when I asked that question.

QUESTIONS

1. Who is the most powerful person you have direct access to? That means you could call them and they would call you back.
2. Another way to think about it is through relationships. Whom do you know that could get you in contact with that person? An example would be that you don't know the governor, but you know someone who does, and that person could get you access to the governor.
3. Who is the most powerful person you think your client has access to?

It's not only that you have power, but that you have access to power. Another way to think about power is what organization you represent. Whatever organization you work for, you represent that organization. From a client standpoint, you have power because you represent the organization that has the power to influence the client's life. Therefore, it's not how you see yourself but how the client sees you. The client will see you as someone with power, influence, and control over their life. Even if you are following policy, you have the power to implement that policy over the client. And that ability alone is more powerful than what the client has. Clients cannot take those policies and influence you or control what you do or say; they are at the mercy of those in power who influence the decisions they make. The client can be questioned how they live their life, if they're making progress to no longer need or graduate from the services they are receiving, all at your discretion.

Therefore, as part of my supervision with staff, I talk about not falling back on the position that you don't have any power—because you do. And the question is how you will use that power to support your client and assist them in resolving the issues that brought them to you. Can you use your power in certain circumstances to turn what could be a long-term relationship into a shorter-term relationship so the client can move on with their life?

## WILLIAM ADMITTING MISTAKES

One of the lessons I had to learn was there is no such thing as perfection, and we are all going to make mistakes. I prided myself on not making mistakes and working hard to be the best worker I could be. From meeting with clients, getting the paperwork in on time, advocating for resources, and assisting my coworkers whenever I could, I tried not to make mistakes. I didn't have a standard of perfection or try to hold others to a standard of perfection. But I didn't want to make any mistakes. I must confess that I have made mistakes and tried to correct them as quickly as possible, but there was a case that I messed up, and I wasn't completely sure of the best way to correct my mistake.

I was assigned a case with a mother who had several mental health issues. She had two boys, and she was having difficulty providing for their daily care. The boy's aunt was trying to help provide care for the family. At one visit, the boys were home alone. Concerned over the five- and eight-year-old boys, the aunt packed their clothes and toys and took them back to her house. Not sure what to do, she called Children's Protective Services, who came out and did an investigation. They decided to place the boys with the aunt and her husband, and I was assigned the case to work with the mother and address the issues which resulted in the boys' removal.

I met with the aunt, her husband, their children, and the two nephews placed with them. Based on my assessment, they were a caring family who provided a stable environment for their children and cared about their nephews. They wanted to provide a safe, caring environment for the nephews with the hope that her sister would get better and her children would return to her care. The boys were happy staying with their aunt and uncle.

I worked with the mother and the boys to find the best supports and resources so the two boys could get the care they needed; I worked for the boys to remain in their same school and looked for ways for them to still have access and interaction with their friends. The aunt and her husband were an easy couple to work with, supportive and caring, and had no problems following the policies necessary when placing children in care.

I had a more difficult time working with the biological mother. Not because of a resistance to treatment—I never got that far. The mother was a difficult person to find. Multiple visits to the house, talking to friends she might associate with, and trying to develop an assessment to put a treatment plan together was extremely difficult. With the children placed with their aunt and uncle, I had 90 days to work with the biological mother, put a treatment plan together, and document progress so that at the court hearing, I could provide an update on the progress the mother had made.

During the first month, I had two meetings with the mother. Meeting with her and explaining my role, the types of services available, developing a treatment plan to get the boys returned to her. After my first two visits, I would make regular stops to the house but could not find her. In the second month, I found myself reducing the number of times I looked for the mother, and as I moved into the third month, I made no visits to the mother's home. A couple of weeks before the court hearing I was putting my report together, and in one of the sections, I had to list the contacts that I had with the foster family, the children, and the mother. While I could document regular contact with the foster family and children, I only had those two contacts with the mother, and as I put the document together, it showed evidence of my lack of trying to contact her after that first month. Because I had two weeks before the court hearing, I started going by the mother's house every day, including weekends, hoping she would be home to give me some additional contacts for my report.

After years of working in the field and testifying in court, I knew that as I talked about the lack of progress the biological mother had made, her attorney would ask about the number of attempts and actual contacts with the mother, my effort (or lack of effort) in trying to reach out to her, and the reason for this lack of contact.

As I prepared the report, it was clear my mistake was the lack of investment that I made in trying to contact the biological mother. Because the children were in a good home, the treatment components were in place for the boys, and with a high caseload, I spent more time on some of the more challenging cases.

I knew the attorney would have a strong case regarding my lack of contact, the judge would not be happy with my answers, and my agency would look embarrassed and unprofessional by my lack of effort to contact the biological mother. Therefore, my options were to document that I've made more contacts then I did because, in my mind, the reality was that I could have gone to the house every day but the mother wasn't going to be there and that was not a good use of my time. Or I can take the consequences and admit my lack of effort in trying to contact the biological mother. This resulted in another issue, since the goal of foster care was reunification. If I made almost no attempts to contact and work with the mother, then I wasn't making any effort toward reunification. I believed the children were better off where they were, and I did not want to place them back into the environment with the biological mother.

My second mistake was that I was deciding what was in the best interest of the children long term when I had not made the investment short term to figure out the best options for both boys.

In the end, I documented my lack of contact with the biological mother in my report and testified to that in court. Mother's attorney, the assistant prosecutor for the county, and the judge were all upset by my lack of time trying to reach out to the biological mother.

I had told my supervisor about my lack of contact before the court hearing, and after the court hearing he placed a reprimand in my file, and as part of my supervision, I had to produce documentation of my contacts with every client on my caseload, which also produced more work for my supervisor. After six months, my supervisor no longer requested the documentation because he believed that I would not make that mistake again. But for the rest of my time at the agency, there was never the complete trust that I once had.

## CODE OF ETHICS

A commitment to best practices in child and family welfare begins with a code of ethics. An excellent example is the National Association of Social workers (NASW) Code of Ethics. The organization provides ethical principles and standards that serve as a foundation for best practices.

Some professions have codes of ethics. Codes of ethics are standards for your profession, the treatment of clients, coworkers, and systems. The goal is always to bring honor to yourself, treat people with dignity and respect, and uphold the principles of your profession.

The different codes of ethics are not designed to have an answer for every situation, but as a model and framework for how to address that issue with the highest possible ethical standards. It is important to learn your code of ethics because it can be a positive tool to assist you in your work and career.

The code of ethics also assists us with our beliefs. What do you personally think about faith, religion, gender differences, L.G.B.T.Q.I.A.+. race, culture, government, politicians, environment, and faith-based organizations? A code of ethics can help balance your beliefs and the beliefs of the client to provide services to the people on your caseload. You don't have to agree with all of their beliefs, and they don't have to agree with all of your beliefs. The question is, can a treatment plan be reasonable so that it meets the needs of the client to achieve the desired outcome?

### QUESTIONS

1. Find and review the code of ethics for the profession you are in or plan on going into. Based on that document, write three paragraphs on what its main purpose is.
2. Discuss with peers who have an interest in other areas how their code of ethics differs from or is the same as yours.

## JANET AND THE TWO MODELS

Most early education and training focused on what we refer to now as a deficit model. A deficit model can be defined as when working with clients, you identify the problems the client is dealing with and develop a plan around those deficits. It does make sense that if you're working with someone, you must identify what the problems or challenges are, or what the purpose of working with them is. It's not a process of making something up, but it is addressing the issues like substance abuse, mental health, domestic violence, or a variety of other challenges impacting the person's ability to address those deficits.

However, what has evolved over the years is the idea of a strength-based model. Like the deficit model, a strength-based model identifies the issues that a person must address. The difference is that in addition to identifying the issues, you identify the strengths that the client has. Those strengths could include how they survive, how they manage difficult situations, or how they've been able to maintain some parts of their life during struggles. All those things are strengths. And the idea of the strength-based model is to take those strengths and use those as the foundation to address the deficits.

My first job out of college was working with several single parents, mostly women who are struggling with issues like employment, getting children to school, having enough resources, not having a stable place to live, homelessness, and getting into relationships where there could be domestic violence, stealing resources, or unstable environments.

In working with the single parents, because of the challenges that the mothers were facing, one of the treatment steps included in every treatment plan was for the mother to attend parenting classes. Years earlier, before I joined the agency, there was an agreement between the agencies, court systems, attorneys, and community funders that the mother's lack of parenting skills was impacting their ability to provide for their children.

As I started working with families and putting treatment plans together, I included the parenting classes. I would go with the parents to some of their parenting classes to see how they were doing and learn the content so I could reinforce that when I was working with the clients in their home.

Over time, what I learned was mothers were dealing with a lot of issues and challenges that were making them feel overwhelmed. But I also found while working with the parents and the children where I could create a bubble in the environment so that there was just parent-child interaction, I noticed most parents knew how to parent their children. They knew what their children's needs were, they knew how to interact with them, they tried to protect and care for them, and they wanted their children to have opportunities that they did not have. I saw it was difficult for the parents to parent when they were also trying to deal with how to protect their children from domestic violence, moving from house to house, and providing the right nutritional foods for their children when they didn't have a place to keep and store food because they had to pack to move quickly.

So, thinking about and reviewing the code of ethics, I realized that if I were putting things in place to make life more stressful for my clients, was I using a deficit model?

As I continued working with my clients, I found that many of them knew how to parent their children; it was the other stressors that were impacting their ability to parent. Therefore, going against the norm, I started developing treatment plans for those clients that did not include parenting classes. My reasoning was if they were attending parenting classes, it meant that they would spend less time on the other stressors impacting their life and attending the parenting classes was just one more stressor.

That position was a difficult sell. My supervisor struggled with that because she included parenting classes in her treatment plans, and all the other people that she supervised always included parenting classes in their treatment plans. She supported my recommendation but thought it would be a tough sell before the judges.

After working with the mother, we put a treatment plan together that I submitted to the judge, clerk, and all the attorneys. At the court hearing, I was sworn in, and generally, the attorneys would ask questions first, followed by the judge. But this time, the judge had the first question. The judge said, "I reviewed the treatment plan and you made a mistake because there were no parenting classes."

This was my chance to explain why I did not include parenting classes in the treatment plan and to see if there was going to be any fallout from the judge and the attorneys. Once I explained my rationale, the judge reluctantly said it was okay not to include the parenting classes in the treatment plan. After several questions from the attorneys, they also agreed with excluding the parenting classes.

This is an example of how strength-based models can help remind us not to do something or include something just because it's always been that way. It challenges us to think about what's in the best interest of the client, not providing services and support that overwhelms clients.

When I started in the field, one of the things I heard people say, especially about low-income families and families where there was neglect or abuse, there was a belief (best practice) that children should not be placed with relatives. An expression I heard a lot was, "The fruit never falls far from the tree." Which means that it's probably not much different from any members of the family, and if there's a problem with the family you are working with, the other members of the family are probably dealing with the same issues or some other issue that would make them inappropriate to care for someone else's children.

Across the country today, you can see where relative placements are our first choice. A change from a deficit-based model to a strength-based model meant that children would stay connected with their family and that those family members could provide appropriate care. There will always be situations where relatives cannot provide care. And there will be situations where relatives are not the best placement. However, we should look at the strengths within a family, within the environment, and a community to see if there are ways that the family can be supported and use that base as the foundation for the treatment plan.

## CONCLUSION

This chapter on best practices is to get you to think about best practices in a variety of ways. It is to gather information, talk to people, become lifelong learners on the skill sets necessary to work with clients. It is to understand that theories, concepts, ideas, and best practices will evolve. Professionals and policy makers have different perceptions of poor people, single parents, people of color, people with disabilities, mental health, and a host of other areas, throughout history, and those beliefs were used to develop treatment plans. We still have laws and policies that are passed based upon one's belief about a certain population as opposed to evidence-based decision making.

Therefore, we want you exposed to a variety of ideas, knowledge, beliefs, and ways of addressing issues so that you come up with the best plan with your clients. If you develop a belief or model that every client fits into, is that in the best interest of the client? If you're an expert in running groups and the only thing you run is groups, whenever clients come to you, you put them in groups. But if you have an understanding of a variety of models and treatment plans, even if you are not an expert in all of them, as you assess the best approaches for your clients, they might not include groups. And because of your understanding, your strength-based perspective, and your code of ethics, you will develop a treatment plan that is in the best interests of the client, not what is most comfortable for you.

Therefore, there is no one best practice. It is the ability to challenge yourself, to learn, to grow, to surround yourself with people with differing opinions to expand your knowledge and understanding, and most important, to understand that while there are several areas in which you may be an expert, the client is always going to be the expert in their own environment. They live it every single day of their life, and the fact they are interacting with you means that they have found a way to survive through all of the chaos, struggles, and challenges. That alone can be your foundation to build a treatment plan in support of your clients. And that is best practice.

## REFERENCES

Austin, M. J. (December 2018). Social work management practice, 1917–2017: A history to inform the future. *Social Service Review 92*(4), 548–616.

Baldwin, M. (2000). Does self-assessment in a group help students to learn? *Social Work Education, 19*(5), 451–462. https://doi-org.ezproxy.gvsu .edu/10.1080/026154700435977

Bandura, A. (1977). Self-efficacy: Toward a unifying theory of behavioral change. *Psychological Review, 84*(2), 191–215. https://doi.org/10.1037/0033-295X.84.2.191

Bandura, A. (1994). Self-efficacy. In V. S Ramachaudran (Ed.), *Encyclopedia of human behavior* (Vol. 4, 71–81). Academic Press. (Reprinted in H. Friedman [Ed.], 1998). Academic Press.

Day, A. G., Somers, C. L., Baroni, B. A., West, S. D., Sanders, L., & Peterson, C. D. (2015). Evaluation of a trauma-informed school intervention with girls in a residential facility school: Student perceptions of school environment. In *Journal of Aggression, Maltreatment and Trauma* (Vol. 24, 1086–1105). Routledge.

Drapalova, E., Belackova, V., Calado, D., Van Dongen, A., Paneva, I., Pavarin, R., ... Grund, J. P. (2019). Early identification of locally emerging trends in psychoactive substance use–experience and best practice in four European localities. *Substance Use and Misuse, 54*(10), 1633–1645.

Gordon, L. (2011). Child welfare: A brief history. *Social Welfare History Project.* Retrieved from http://socialwelfare.library.vcu.edu/programs/child-welfare-overview/

Grise-Owens, E., Miller, J., Escobar-Ratliff, L., & George, N. (2018). Teaching note—teaching self-care and wellness as a professional practice skill: A curricular case example. *Journal of Social Work Education, 54*(1), 180–186. Retrieved from http://search.proquest.com.ezproxy.gvsu.edu/docview/2034280191?accountid=39473

Kessler, M. L., Gira, E., & Poertner, J. (2005). Moving best practice to evidence-based practice in child welfare. *Families in Society, 86*(2), 244–250.

Knight, D. K., Joe, G. W., Morse, D. T., Smith, C., Knudsen, H., Johnson, I., ... Wiley, T. R. A. (2019). Organizational context and individual adaptability in promoting perceived importance and use of best practices for substance use. *Journal of Behavioral Health Services and Research, 46*(2), 192–216.

Minas, M., Ribeiro, M. T., & Anglin, J. P. (2019). Social and community program approaches to participants: Exploring best practices. *Journal of Community Psychology, 47*(2), 398–413.

O'Neill, M., Yoder Slater, G., & Batt, D. (2019). Social work student self-care and academic stress. *Journal of Social Work Education, 55*(1), 141–152. doi:http://dx.doi .org.ezproxy.gvsu.edu/10.1080/10437797.2018.1491359

Romanelli, L. H., Landsverk, J., Levitt, J. M., Leslie, L. K., Hurley, M. M., Bellonci, C., ... Jensen, P. S. (2009). Best practices for mental health in child welfare: Screening, assessment, and treatment guidelines. *Child Welfare, 88*(1), 163–188.

Serbati, S. (2017). You won't take away my children! Families' participation in child protection. Lessons since a best practice. *Children and Youth Services Review,* (82), 214–221.

# ABOUT THE EDITORS

**Jerry L. Johnson, Ph.D., MSW** is an associate professor in the School of Social Work at Grand Valley State University in Grand Rapids, Michigan. He received his MSW from Grand Valley State University and his Ph.D. in sociology from Western Michigan University. Johnson has been in the human services field since 1983, serving as a family therapist, clinical supervisor, administrator, consultant, teacher, trainer, and author. He was the recipient of two Fulbright Scholarship awards to Albania in 1998-99 and 2000-01. In addition to teaching and writing, Johnson serves in various consulting capacities in countries such as Albania, Armenia, and China.

He is the author of two previous books, Crossing Borders—Confronting History: Intercultural Adjustment in a Post-Cold War World (2000, Rowan and Littlefield) and Fundamentals of Substance Abuse Practice (2004, Wadsworth Brooks/Cole).

**George Grant, Jr., Ph.D., LMSW** is the dean of the College of Community and Public Service and a professor in the School of Social Work at Grand Valley State University in Grand Rapids, Michigan. He received his BSW from Marygrove College, MSW from Grand Valley State University, and Ph.D. in sociology from Western Michigan University. Grant, Jr. is a professor, administrator, evaluator, practitioner, consultant, and committed to community engagement primary in the fields of child welfare.

Dr. Johnson and Dr. Grant are the editors of a previous eight-volume casebook series, including: Substance Abuse (2005), Mental Health (2005), Foster Care (2005), Adoption (2005), Domestic Violence (2005), Community Practice (2005), Medical Social Work (2005), and Sexual Abuse (2007).

# ABOUT THE AUTHORS

**George Grant, Jr., PhD, LMSW**, is the Dean of the College of Community and Public Service and professor in the School of Social Work at Grand Valley State University in Grand Rapids, Michigan. He received his BSW from Marygrove College, MSW from Grand Valley State University, and PhD in sociology from Western Michigan University. Grant Jr. is a professor, administrator, evaluator, practitioner, consultant, and committed to community engagement primarily in the field of child welfare.

**Jessica R. Campbell, LMSW** is the Program Coordinator and Independent Living Skills Coach for the Gayle R. Davis Center for Women and Gender Equity's Fostering Laker Success Program. She works with youth who have experienced foster care who currently attend Grand Valley State University. She received her bachelor's degree in Nonprofit Management and Public Administration from Grand Valley State University and a master's degree in Social Work at Eastern Michigan University. She is a part of several knowledge communities in the National Association of Student Personnel Administrators and serves as a Niara mentor.

CPSIA information can be obtained
at www.ICGtesting.com
Printed in the USA
LVHW020405080722
722987LV00002B/24